THE TROPICAL AGRICULTURALIST

Series Editor

René Coste

President of the IRCC

D1647021

Upland Rice

Michel Jacquot

Brigitte Courtois

Translated by Paul Skinner

MACMILLAN
PUBLISHERS

Original French edition published 1983 under the title
Le Riz Pluvial in the series *Le Technicien d'Agriculture
Tropicale*, by the ACCT and Maisonneuve et Larose; 15, rue
Victor-Cousin, 75 005 Paris, FRANCE.
No responsibility is taken by the holders of the copyright for any changes
to the original French text.

This edition published by *Macmillan Publishers Ltd*
London and Basingstoke.
*Associated companies and representatives in Accra,
Auckland, Delhi, Dublin, Gaborone, Hamburg, Harare,
Hong Kong, Kuala Lumpur, Lagos, Manzini, Melbourne,
Mexico City, Nairobi, New York, Singapore, Tokyo*

Published in co-operation with The Technical Centre for
Agricultural and Rural Co-operation, POB 380,
6700 AJ Wageningen, The Netherlands.

Printed in Hong Kong

British Library Cataloguing in Publication Data
Jacquot, Michel
   Upland rice. — (The Tropical
   agriculturalist).
   1. Upland rice — Tropics
   I. Title   II. Courtois, Brigitte   III. Series
   IV. Le riz pluvial. *English*
   633.1'8'09143   SB191.R5

ISBN 0-333-44889-8

Contents

Acknowledgements

All photographs are courtesy of the authors.
The publishers have made every effort to trace the copyright holders, but if they have overlooked any, they will be pleased to make the necessary arrangements at the first opportunity.
Cover photograph courtesy of Oxford Scientific Films: photograph by M.J.Coe

A new collection: the tropical agriculturalist

The Agency for Cultural and Technical Cooperation has always given the preparation, dissemination and exchange of scientific and technical information a high priority in its programmes of scientific and technical cooperation. This kind of information is a major feature of the dialogue between cultures and is a key factor of development. It has made an effort to set up data banks and organise them in networks; to arrange ministerial conferences, seminars and symposia; and to publish technical handbooks, scientific works and catalogues, particularly in recent years, in the field of rural development and agriculture for developing countries.

With this in mind, the CTA and Editions Maisonneuve et Larose produced a series of books under the title 'Le Technicien D'Agriculture Tropicale', originally published in French and covering tropical areas in Francophone Africa. The CTA have translated this series into English for publication by Macmillan Publishers, and it has been extended to make it relevant to Anglophone Africa. These books have been designed, written and illustrated in such a way as to provide practical, easily consulted handbooks, in which development workers and farmers will find, expressed in clear, vivid language, techniques and advice for improving crops, and hence yields, and, in a general manner, for farming their land better and thus contributing to the food self-sufficiency of their country.

The editor of the collection would like to express his deep thanks to Mr. F.Bour, Director-General of IRAT, and Mr. J.Cuillé, Director-General of IRFA, for the interest which they have shown in this collection.

Introduction

This work was written in order to provide an answer to the following three questions:

What is 'Upland rice'?

Where can it be grown?

What varieties should be used and what cultivation techniques?

Hence the following chapters:

- Basic ideas:
  - different types of rice cultivation;
  - cropping systems with upland rice;
  - major constraints;
  - where should upland rice be grown?
  - the rice plant.
- Selection of varieties.
- Cultivation techniques:
  - rotations in the cultivation of upland rice;
  - land preparation;
  - fertilisation;
  - sowing;
  - weed control;
  - pests of upland rice;
  - harvesting, threshing, drying, preservation;
  - time taken to perform different operations,

together with a glossary and the sources used.

This handbook has been made possible thanks to the publications and technical data sheets of IRAT[1] (particularly those by Mr. Vallée), CEEMAT[2] and also WARDA[3].

The nature of the information used means that this work is more specifically intended for African countries.

---

1 IRAT: Institut de recherches Agronomiques Tropicales et des Cultures Vivrieres -Institute for Tropical Agricultural Research and Food Crops.
2 CEEMAT: Centre d'Etudes et d'Expérimentation du Machinisme Agricole Tropical.
3 WARDA: West Africa Rice Development Association

It was written by B.Courtois under the guidance of Mr. M. Jacquot, with the help of IRAT specialists, particularly Mr. Birie-Habas, Mr. Brenière, Mr. Ducreux, Mr. Guis, Mr. Pocthier, Mr. Poisson, Mr. Seguy and Mr. Vallée.

The author also received the advice of Mr. M.Mahdavi, Technical Director of the CFDT[4].

4   CFDT: Compagnie Française des Textiles.

1 Different types of rice cultivation

One of the most original features of rice is the fact that it can be grown under very different environmental conditions, particularly from the point of view of its water supply. It can be grown either as an upland crop, supplied solely by rainwater, or, at the other end of the scale, as a floating crop, in a sheet of water which may be several metres deep, all the intermediate stages being possible. Thus the main classifications are based on this criterion. A nomenclature adapted to Africa is that of WARDA, which distinguishes between two basic types, lowland rice and upland rice.

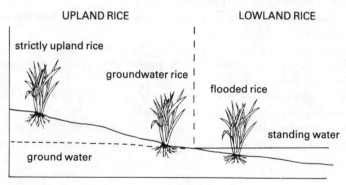

Fig 1 *Diagram showing the position of different types of rice cultivation without water control*

Lowland rice

This term encompasses all types of rice cultivation where the soil is covered with water to a variable depth over a period which may extend to cover the whole of the rice cycle. A distinction is made between: Mangrove rice cultivation and fresh water rice cultivation.

Mangrove rice cultivation

The mangrove is a particular area of vegetation consisting mainly of mangrove forest and found in the lowland areas of river estuaries or along the coast. Periodically invaded by saltwater, it poses a number of very specific problems, such as salinity and acidification of the soil.

This type of rice cultivation accounts for some 10% of the rice-growing area in Africa.

The countries where large areas are given over to this type of cultivation are mainly Guinea-Bissau, Sierra Leone, The Gambia, Nigeria and Senegal, i.e., approximately 200 000 ha for West Africa.

Freshwater rice cultivation

Depending on the degree of water management achieved, it is possible to differentiate between two types.

Rice cultivation without water control

The farmer exercises no control over the water supply to the rice, which is provided by rainwater or by the rise in the level of a river in a flood plain. However, he can retain some of this water by installing bunds or levelling the ground according to the contours of the land. This practice is very widespread in Asia (India, Thailand, etc.).

Submersion may occur at any stage of the growth cycle and the water vary in depth.

Floating rice is an extreme case and may be grown under water which is sometimes very deep indeed, which means that special fast-growing varieties have to be used.

In West Africa floating rice cultivation is particularly developed in, for example, Northern Nigeria and Sierra Leone.

Rice cultivation without water control accounts for 22.5% of the rice-growing area in Africa, which means that this type is second in importance in the region.

Rice cultivation with water control

Man has contrived, to ensure artificially, that the water requirements of rice are met throughout its cycle, either by means of gravity the most simple system – or by pumping.

Levelling, depending on how rigorously it is carried out, makes it possible to control the level of water in the rice field. Moreover the water engineering structures may make it possible to dry out the land. This may be necessary in order to spread fertiliser or herbicides, or for harvesting.

Although highly developed in Asia, particularly in China, rice cultivation, with water control, was introduced only recently in Africa. Here it covers less than 5% of the rice-growing area. Its wider use is limited by the high costs of installing and maintaining the hydroagricultural facilities required.

Upland rice

Upland rice cultivation is practised on land which is covered, only very exceptionally, by standing water.

Strictly upland rice cultivation

This is found on well-drained soils above the flood-line, where the water supply is provided solely by rain and the soil's retention capacity. It is frequently grown both in steeply sloping areas or on gently undulating hillsides.

Worldwide, 16 million hectares are given over to upland rice cultivation. Brazil alone accounts for 4.5 million hectares, which makes it the world's leading producer of this type of rice. The Asian countries, however, which in fact give over only a fairly small proportion of their rice-growing area to this type of production, grow nearly 9 million hectares of rice in this way.

Importance of strictly upland rice cultivation in the world

Continent	Total rice-growing area*	Upland rice area*	Upland rice as proportion of total rice-growing area
Africa	2.0	1.2	60%
Asia	128.5	9.0	7%
Latin America	7.3	5.3	73%
WORLD TOTAL	143.6	16.0	11%

* in millions of hectares

The cultivation of strictly upland rice is the dominant type of production in Africa, where it accounts for 60% of the area given over to to rice-growing, i.e., some 1.2 million hectares. This area is divided up among certain major producer countries as follows:

Sierra Leone	239 000 ha,
Ivory Coast	392 000 ha,
Liberia	180 000 ha,
Guinea-Bissau	38 000 ha,
Zaire	250 000 ha,
Nigeria	140 000 ha,
Madagascar	100 000 ha.

Fig 2 *Upland rice in Africa*

Where the rice is grown in the traditional way, the yield is generally fairly low – of the order of 1 t/ha, and often below that. Where it is grown intensively, the yield may be as much as 2.5 t/ha, or even higher, depending on local conditions. The cultivation of upland rice, as with any other upland crop, is subject to the vagaries of climate and the results are therefore more uncertain than those of rice grown under irrigation.

Groundwater rice

The water supply to the rice is often partly provided from groundwater close to the surface to the soil, into which the plant dips its roots.

This type of rice cultivation is encountered either at the foot of slopes, or in areas where an impermeable layer creates particularly satisfactory conditions.

Benefiting from two potential sources of water, groundwater rice cultivation generally has a higher, more regular yield than strictly upland rice.

Groundwater rice cultivation is not very widespread in Africa, with only 2.5% of the area given over to rice growing.

The table below summarizes the different types of rice cultivation encountered in Africa and the position they occupy. Our remarks in the following pages will be confined to strictly upland rice, in view of its relative importance.

Different types of rice cultivation in Africa and their importance
(source: WARDA)

Type of rice cultivation	Relative importance of each type of rice cultivation in Africa (in %)
LOWLAND RICE	
mangrove rice	10.0
freshwater rice	
– without water control	22.5
– with water control	5.0
UPLAND RICE	
strictly upland rice	60.0
groundwater rice	2.5

2 Basic cultivation systems for upland rice

The basic cultivation systems used for upland rice are of three major types:
shifting systems,
pioneer systems,
fixed systems.

Shifting system

Shifting cultivation is a very widespread traditional system and is the dominant method of production in Africa.

The farmer clears a plot of land, which is often quite small. Because only very simple tools are usually available, he generally only cuts down shrubs, bushes and small trees, leaving untouched the larger trees. This permits good and rapid regrowth of the vegetation after the plot has been abandoned.

The farmer then burns all this vegetation. Burning is a very important stage for ensuring that the land is properly cleaned and limiting the extent of the weeds. Timing is critical, the burning usually being done at the start of the rainy season.

The working of the soil is cursory, often being confined to simply turning over the surface layer of the soil with a hoe. The seed is then sown, generally six to eight seeds to a seed-hole. Often the sowing is staggered so that if the plants encounter a period of drought, those which have not reached a critical stage of their development will have a chance of surviving. For the same reason, the farmer may also sow simultaneously, varieties with different growth cycles. Sowing density is traditionally low.

With shifting cultivation, intercropping is common practice. Rice is grown with maize, manioc, yams, spices, etc.

Certain seeds are sometimes sown together in the same seed-hole. Manioc and yams are simply intercropped between the rice plants.

Two operations require a certain amount of attention:

Fig 3   *Clearing the land*

(i) weeding
Although during the first year weeds are not too much of a problem, if successive crops of rice are grown the plot may be invaded by weeds, this is one of the main causes of falling yields. Weeding is done entirely by hand. If it is carried out too late, it may give rise to labour problems which will be difficult to overcome.

(ii) control of birds
It is necessary to guard the crop carefully.

The final operation is harvesting, which is also done by hand. Only the panicles are collected, which means that this can be done in any weather. The harvesting is staggered both because of the techniques adopted for sowing and also because, in some cases, only amounts which can be taken back to the village in the evening are harvested.

After one or two years of production, the problems due to this type of production (invasion by weeds, lowering of the fertility of the soil, etc.) become so great that the plots have to be abandoned.

Under the traditional system, the land was able to lie fallow for eight to ten years, this permitted good regrowth of the vegetation. For some years

Fig 4 *Burning the vegetation*

the length of the fallow period has been declining: because of demographic pressure it is no longer possible to let land lie fallow. Farmers therefore return to plots much more quickly (three to five years), which no longer enables fertility to be adequately maintained.

Furthermore, the demand from consumers is steadily increasing because of growing urbanization. The yields obtained with traditional shifting cultivation of rice are too low to meet the demand satisfactorily. Attempts have therefore been made to intensify production.

It would seem that farmers must adopt a more settled way of life if they are to develop a higher-yielding system. How else could they contemplate careful land preparation, erosion control, and fertilisation, if they intended to abandon the plot within the year?

Pioneer system

Rice may be grown as a pioneer crop in two ways:
(i) after the land has been cleared, the rice may be grown as an improving

8

crop, prior to the planting of a pasture mixture. This type of rice cultivation is found in Brazil in particular, but also occasionally in Africa (Ivory Coast) and Madagascar;

(ii) rice may be grown as a cover crop in young fruit (coffee, cacao, citrus and rubber trees, etc.) or forest plantations. This type of rice cultivation is to be found in Japan, Brazil, Ivory Coast, Thailand, etc.

These two types of cultivation are grouped together here, because they share an important characteristic: both consider the cereal merely as a temporary by-product, an adjunct to the main crop. At the same time, however, it meets the local inhabitants' need for food.

Fig 5   *Intercropping of upland rice between young coffee trees*

Both systems also involve moving the rice cultivation: in the first case, on to fallow land. Sometimes this extends to regions where the growing of upland rice becomes precarious; and in the second case, to young plantations.

9

Fixed system

All forms of fixed rice cultivation observe a number of rules:
- fertilisation, depending on the plants' requirements,
- avoiding excessively rapid impoverishment of the soil,
- accompanying anti-erosion measures,
- rotation with legumes,
- measures to combat weed infestation,

in order to make the return on the investment in fertilisers, herbicides or labour worthwhile, varieties must be selected that enable yields of at least 2.5 t/ha to be obtained. Intensive cultivation systems are possible as specific cultivation techniques have been developed.

Some examples will give an idea of the different approaches which may be encountered throughout the world. The systems are classified according to the degree of mechanization (manual cultivation, animal-drawn tillage, partly or completely mechanized cultivation, etc.).

(a) Animal-drawn tillage

Very careful land preparation is undertaken, which may follow the contour-lines: the soil is ploughed twice and then disc-harrowed three times with implements drawn by a buffalo.

The seed is broadcast into furrows made by a tine harrow or 'lithao', the seed then being covered by a levelling harrow.

Maintenance of the crop is done mainly by hand but the extent of the preparation limits weed infestation. No fertiliser is applied. Harvesting is done by hand.

The rice is often grown as part of a rotation (maize, beans, etc.).

(b) Semi-mechanized cultivation

Land preparation and sowing are mechanized, the soil being ploughed and then harrowed. A drill is used for sowing. Weeding and harvesting are, however, still done by hand. The use of fertiliser and herbicides is limited.

The rice is grown as part of a rotation with other crops (cotton, maize, yams, etc.).

(c) Fully mechanized cultivation

Here the rice is grown on a large scale and cultivation is mechanized from start to finish. Improved seed, fertiliser, herbicides and other products for treating the crop are commonly used, sometimes being spread by aeroplane. This type of rice cultivation is similar to the industrial scale rice-cultivation practised in the United States or Australia.

3 Major constraints

By 'major constraints' is meant curbs to the development of upland rice cultivation, either in terms of extending the area or in terms of intensification.

Weeds

With the shifting cultivation systems, after a patch of forest land, that has been allowed to lie fallow, has been burned, weeds are not much of a problem. However, they start to become a problem with successive crops; from the third or fourth year onwards, the plot becomes invaded by weeds to such an extent that, in most cases, it has to be abandoned.

With a fixed system, weeds are one of the major constraints and require constant control. Here, unlike the case where rice is grown in standing water, one fails to benefit from the effective controls of transplantation and submersion. However, it is possible to restrict invasion by harmful plants; by hand weeding, mechanical or chemical control, or by a combination of methods.

Reduction in the fertility of soils

With the traditional systems, the crops benefit from reserves accumulated when the land was under forest and the contribution to the soil made by burning the vegetation. This initial fertility is, however, only temporary. In the absence of supplementary fertilisation and the incorporation of crop residues, the soil soon becomes infertile. This is followed by a subsequent substantial drop in yields.

The invasion by weeds was one of the reasons for shifting cultivation, allowing the land to lie fallow being the only method of regeneration known to peasant farmers.

In order to maintain the richness of the soil on a lasting basis and obtain high yields, it is necessary to apply artificial fertiliser (nitrogen, phos-

11

phorus, potassium) and, if possible, organic fertiliser (manure, compost, etc.) and to return crop residues to the soil.

In some cases, the low natural fertility is compounded by problems of toxicity related to the high level of acidity in the soil, which tend to reduce yields. These problems may be rectified by means of additions containing lime.

Fig 6   *Example of damage caused by drought*

Drought

Upland rice depends on local conditions for its water supply: if rainfall is inadequate or irregular, or if the soil does not retain the water, the crops requirements will not be satisfied and yields will suffer.

Upland rice should preferably be cultivated in areas where there are good soils and abundant rainfall.

It is also prudent to use varieties which will tolerate the uncertainties of climate. Preference should be given to those varieties with stable yields rather than to those which may produce very high yields if the conditions are right but disastrous yields in a bad year.

It is also possible to employ cultural practices such as: careful preparation of the soil, permitting filtration of the rain, or the creation of anti-erosion banks to reduce the risk of run-off.

Diseases

Some diseases are very dangerous for rice. In Africa, the most serious is blast, which can, in the case of very susceptible varieties, completely destroy the growing crop. Blast attacks the leaves and panicles.

In the case of upland rice, this disease is often more serious than where rice is grown under irrigation with good water control. In order to prevent excessive loss of yield, it is imperative to use varieties which offer high and lasting resistance to this disease, as chemical control is particularly expensive.

Other diseases may also cause considerable damage, such as leaf scald, brown spot and sheath rot.

These diseases, with their characteristic symptoms and the specific means of controlling them, are described in a volume entitled 'Main rice

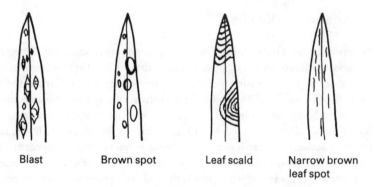

| Blast | Brown spot | Leaf scald | Narrow brown leaf spot |

Fig 7   *Foliar lesions characteristic of the principal rice diseases*

diseases in West Africa' produced by two IRAT researchers and published by WARDA.

The work of the research institutes has made it possible to select varieties with satisfactory resistance to these diseases, so the problem is not as bad as it was. The same institutes are carefully monitoring the development of other diseases which could appear where crops are grown on a large scale and present a threat for the future.

Insects

The main damage to crops is caused by insects which attack the stems or by those which eat the leaves.

In the case of caterpillar pests, insecticides should be used to stem the invasion. This practice proves to be effective and inexpensive.

The damage caused by other insects is at present generally not serious enough to justify chemical means of control.

The research institutes are endeavouring to select varieties which are sufficiently tolerant of the main insects to safeguard the future.

Birds

Birds are definitely one of the major pests. The damage they cause may be enormous. No effective means of control is known at present. The most widespread practice consists of having the plot guarded while the grains are maturing. There does, however, exist in Senegal and the Sahel countries an organization which is responsible for destroying the places where queleas roost.

Harvesting problems

Where all the above constraints have been overcome, the farmer can expand the fixed system of upland rice cultivation either by increasing the area sown or by increasing yields. In order to increase the cultivated area, he will need to develop mechanised cultivation, the chemical control of weeds and various technical solutions, (see the chapters on cultivation techniques). However, work still remains to be done with regard to mechanization; in particular, appropriate harvesting equipment is not available for medium-sized farms (from three to fifteen ha). The research institutes are aware of this problem and are endeavouring to produce intermediate equipment which is less expensive and less cumbersome than the combine harvester but with a similar performance (in particular simultaneous harvesting and threshing).

Lack of economic incentive

Upland rice is generally grown by small farmers for their own needs. For production to increase and to be able to meet the food requirements of the urban population, it is essential that farmers are encouraged to produce amounts surplus to their own needs.

The price of rice must therefore be remunerative and the marketing network well structured. These types of arrangements are currently being made in many countries.

Rice production potential is high in Africa. One of the key factors in the success of a rice-growing project is the organization of marketing networks.

4 Where to grow upland rice

Rainfall

Before planting upland rice, it is important to know two things with regard to climate:

(i) average rainfall during the growth period
(ii) the regularity of the rainfall

The water requirements of upland rice depend primarily on the length of the cycle of the variety being grown and the local climate, which determines the extent of transpiration from the plant.

Generally, the water requirement ranges from 450 mm for short-cycle varieties to 650 mm for long-cycle varieties. During the critical phase from heading to the milky grain stage, water requirements are high, generally of the order of 5 mm to 6 mm per day. This critical phase must therefore coincide with when rainfall is adequate to cover these requirements. Rainfull needs to be regular, particulary in the case of soils with a poor capacity for storing water.

In practice, because of the losses due to run-off and drainage, it is unusual to be able to grow upland rice in areas where average rainfall during the growing period is less than 800 mm without the assistance of groundwater or supplementary irrigation.

Soils

If rainfall is adequate and it follows a regular pattern, the range of soils in which upland rice can be grown is fairly wide. However, if the rainfall cannot be relied upon, it is necessary to choose a soil which can compensate for this, a soil with a high water-retention capacity.

Certain factors enable soils to store water well and to give it up readily:
- **the clay, silt and sand content** (the 'texture'); balanced soils, i.e., soils

containing more or less equal proportions of clay, silt and sand, are the most suitable;
- **the depth;**
- **the geographical location:** for instance, a deep soil with a balanced texture at the foot of a slope provides a good reservoir of water.

Gradients

In some countries, erosion is a considerable problem, since upland rice is often grown on the sides of steeply sloping hills or mountains. There is then a very high risk of gully erosion.

Fairly simple techniques exist for controlling this:

- **appropriate working of the soil** (timing, intensity, etc.),
- **sowing density, covering of the soil** which make it possible to reduce the seriousness of the erosion.

Fig 8   *Gully erosion*

However, in any case, where the gradient is steeper than 1 in 33, buffer strips must be established. These are strips 1 m to 3 m wide following the contour lines and with as much perennial vegetative cover as possible. These strips prevent water from running off onto the slopes, picking up speed and thereby carrying the soil away.

The steeper the gradient, the smaller the distance between the buffer strips: for a gradient of 1 in 2 a buffer strip should be established every 20 m: for a gradient of 1 in 10 one would be needed every 15 m. Where the soils are particularly fine, the buffer strips should be even closer together.

Fig 9   *Contour farming*

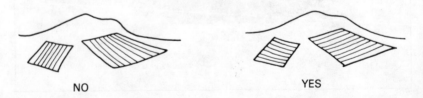

NO   YES

Fig 10   *Cropping along the contour line*

If the cultivation is mechanized, the buffer strips must be relatively parallel so as to correspond to a number of complete passes of the machinery, the contour lines being followed as best as possible. A compromise should therefore be found between these two requirements.

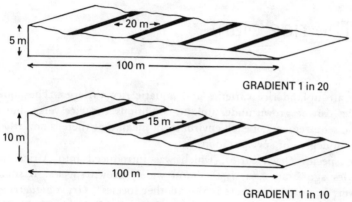

Fig 11   *Buffer strips*

5 The rice plant

There are upland rice varieties and aquatic rice varieties. The aquatic varieties can be grown under upland conditions and vice versa, but the specific requirements of each environment mean that there is nevertheless a certain degree of specialization.

The species *Oryza sativa*, which was introduced into Africa some centuries ago from Asia, is the most widely grown species. It should, however, be noted that there is also another species - *Oryza glaberrima* - which originated in Africa and is to be found in all types of cultivation. It is distinguished from *Oryza sativa* by its short, truncated ligule.

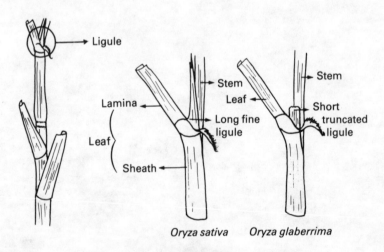

Oryza sativa   *Oryza glaberrima*

Fig 12   *A comparison of the structure of different species of upland rice*

Here we shall only deal with the cultivated varieties of *Oryza sativa*, both traditional and improved.

In Africa, the large, traditional, varieties of the species *Oryza sativa* can be divided up into two major groups:

(i) varieties generally grown under upland conditions, the 'upland' types

These include Moroberekan or LAC 23, which are relatively low-tillering varieties, with long wide leaves, heavy panicles and long wide grains;

(ii) lowland varieties of the 'indica' type

Examples are Gambiaka or Ebandioulaye, which, in contrast, have a good tillering ability and have long fine leaves and long narrow grains.

The selected varieties are: either of tall stature, such as the traditional varieties:

- (OS 6, 63–83 are selected upland varieties, IM 16 is a lowland variety:) or short in stature, such as: IRAT 13, a medium-sized variety for upland rice, IR 8, a semi-dwarf adapted to aquatic rice cultivation.

Still with the species *Oryza sativa*, there is a type normally referred to as 'japonica', a medium-tillering variety with fairly short, fine leaves and short, round grains. This variety is not very widespread in Africa. However, there are varieties selected from crosses between 'upland' and japonica types, such as IRAT 10, which are therefore intermediate strains.

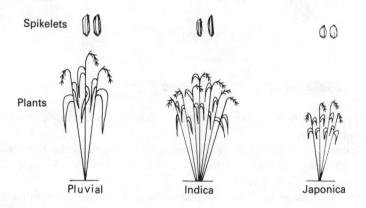

Fig 13   *Different varieties of the species* Oryza Sativa

The growth cycle of rice has a number of stages:

(a) Approximately five days after sowing, emergence takes place, i.e., the plantlets emerge from the soil.

(b) Tillering, i.e., when the plant sends out secondary shoots; this starts about twenty days after sowing.

(c) At a given stage in the cycle, which varies according to variety and the date of sowing, the panicles develop (panicle initiation), then rise up the stem: this is the 'booting' stage, which is followed by emergence of the panicles from the leaf sheaths ('heading' stage).

Fig 14 *Upland rice fifteen days after sowing*

there is generally a period of thirty days between panicle initiation and heading.

(d) Immediately after heading, flowering takes place and the rice flowers ('spikelets') are self-pollinated. Self-fertilisation is the rule and cross-pollination is rare.

(e) The next stage is when the grains ripen. Some thirty to thirty five days after heading, the grains reach maturity and are ready to be harvested.

The total length of the cycle varies according to variety. It depends on the period of time between sowing and heading, – the mature stage differing little from one variety to another;

if the period is relatively short (less than 80 days), the varieties are early;

if it is relatively long (in excess of 105 days), the variety are late;

if it is intermediate (between 80 and 105 days), the varieties are medium-cycle.

Within the same variety, the rice cycle may often last a few days longer if the plant is subjected to periods of drought.

With certain varieties, the tillering stage may continue after the panicle initiation stage. Should that happen, the last tiller will reach maturity

Fig 15   *Upland rice after fourty five days*

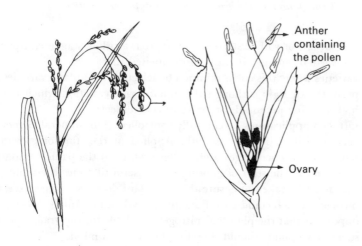

Fig 16   *Rice spikelet*

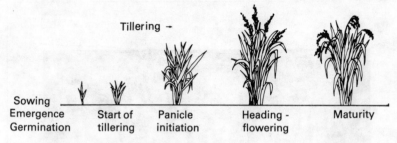

Tillering →

Sowing
Emergence   Start of   Panicle   Heading -   Maturity
Germination   tillering   initiation   flowering

Fig 17   *Rice growth cycle*

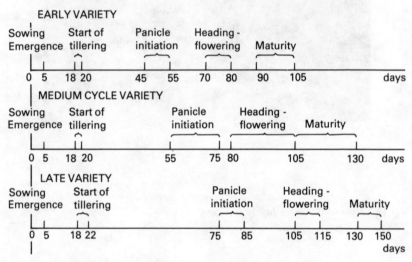

Fig 18   *A comparison of the growth cycles of different varieties*

after the others or will be sterile. Thus there is a risk of staggered ripening or of a waste of energy. It is therefore advised that:

(i) varieties where this risk is minimal be selected: the upland varieties are perfectly all right although the aquatic rice varieties, which have a high tillering potential, are risky in this respect;

(ii) nitrogen applications be carefully controlled. This mineral element is very important for rice growth. Applied at the start of growth in particular, it encourages useful tillering but, at the panicle initiation stage and at the start of booting when useful tillering is established, care must be taken to ensure that the plant does not receive excessive nitrogen, which could encourage the growth of new tillers. Lastly, it is important that the plant has nitrogen available for the grain-ripening stage. Two points should therefore be borne in mind:

(a) the idea of splitting nitrogenous fertiliser dressings;

(b) the idea of timing the applications.

24

Knowledge of the rice cycle is important as it helps determine fairly precisely certain aspects of the cultural techniques.

Similarly, the plant's water requirements are not identical throughout the growth period. At certain times, rice demands larger quantities of water, as is shown in the diagram below.

Thus emergence only takes place at the right time if the land is wet. During tillering, as the plants are still small, a short drought is not too important except in the case of varieties which are susceptible to blast, which is aggravated by drought. However, *twenty days either side of heading the plant is extremely sensitive to lack of water.* At the end of ripening, a drought can be a good thing.

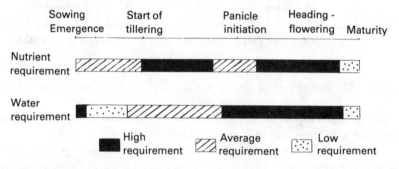

Fig 19   *Requirements of rice during the growth cycle*

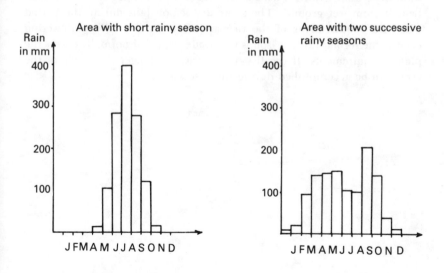

Fig 20   *Examples of monthly distribution of rainfall (average over a number of years)*

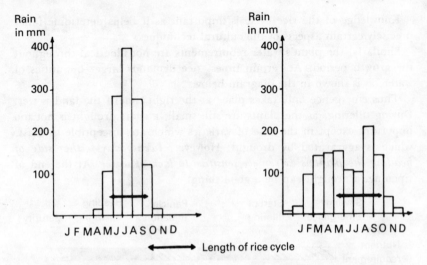

Fig 21   *The growth cycle of upland rice as a function of the rainfall distribution*

Knowledge of these requirements makes it possible to choose the sowing date for a given variety in order to adapt it to a given climate.

Thus, in areas where the rainy season runs from June to September sowing is carried out in June so that both emergence and flowering stages are guaranteed an adequate supply of water.

In areas, where, there are two successive rainy seasons, interrupted by a short dry season, sowing is done at the end of the first rains so that the seeds benefit from wet ground. The short dry season falls during the period when the requirements of the rice are relatively low. When flowering occurs, the second rainy season is well under way and normally covers the plant's requirements. If the first rainy season is longer the whole of the cycle can be accomplished during the first season.

6 Selection of varieties

The possible choices offered here concern only low-altitude areas (less than 800 m).

The adoption of a variety is determined primarily by two criteria: varieties must be found which are adapted to the natural environment and adapted to the cropping system.

Adaptation to the natural environment is evaluated in terms of:

the length of the cycle, which must depend on the length of the rainy season

resistance to pests, particular diseases such as blast, and insects;

resistance to forseeable periods of drought or, alternatively, to poor inslation in very wet regions

adaptation to the major ecological regions savannas or forests;

soil coverage:

In order to control erosion and afford a good degree of competition with weeds, varieties should be sought which rapidly cover the soil or whose plant cover soon closes up.

A variety which possesses these qualities is not really of interest unless it also shows stable resistance to pests. It has been found that varieties which were considered resistant to blast became susceptible to it after a number of years. These were mainly varieties selected for aquatic rice cultivation. In contrast, certain varieties have always retained a high level of resistance. A fair number of traditional varieties grown as an upland crop in Africa (Moroberekan, 63–83, etc.) or varieties selected from this material, such as IRAT 13 and IRAT 112 also possess stable resistance to the disease.

With regard to adaptation to forestry or savanna regions, the varieties currently available may be suitable. The research institutes are, however, endeavouring to select varieties which are more specifically adapted to each of these two major regions.

Adaptation to the cropping system can be assessed at a number of levels:

(i) the degree of intensification

If the yield sought is of the order of 1.5 to 2.5 t/ha, it is preferable to opt for relatively hardy material, which may be fairly tall, i.e., varieties such as Moroberekan, Iguape Cateto, 63–83.

If the yield target is 2.0 to 3.5 t/ha, in areas where rainfall is abundant and regular, it is necessary to select a strain which gives a good response to fertiliser and offers either high resistance to lodging or is short: IRAT 10, IRAT 13 or IRAT 112 would be suitable.

(ii) type of mechanization

For manual harvesting, fairly tall, non-hairy varieties are sought with just a few large panicles, so as to reduce harvesting time and make the task easier. For mechanical harvesting it is important that ripening is concentrated over a short period of time and that the variety offers good resistance to shattering.

There is a wide range of varieties with these characteristics. A particular variety will be adopted according to which of the criteria is accorded priority. It should be noted that at present there are still no varieties

Fig 22   *Upland rice panicle*

available which are well adapted to high-altitude regions.

It may be of interest of give brief details of a number of varieties which are well known in West Africa or Latin America, together with their features, qualities and shortcomings.

MOROBEREKAN: Origin: traditional variety from Ivory Coast.
Average yield* : 2.0 t/ha
Maximum yield* : 4.0 t/ha
Period from sowing to heading: 110 days
Growth cycle: 145 days
Height: 145 cm
Strong points
hardiness
resistant to shattering
resistant to blast
tolerance of stem-borers.
Weak points
susceptibility to lodging
fairly high susceptibility to leaf scald.

IAC 25: Origin: selected in Brazil, descended from a cross between Dourado Precoce and IAC 1 246
Average yield: 1.8 t/ha
Maximum yield: 3.0 t/ha
Period from sowing to heading: 75 days
Growth cycle: 100 days
Height: 145 cm
Strong points
earliness
grain quality
Weak points
low productivity
susceptibility to lodging.

IRAT 13: Origin: mutant of 63–83.
Average yield: 2.5 t/ha
Maximum yield: 5.0 t/ha
Period from sowing to heading: 95 days
Growth cycle: 125 days
Height: 115 cm
Strong points
good adaptability

---

* The average yield is an average of the yields obtained in various locations where the crop has been grown on a large scale. The maximum yield is the yield obtained with good climatic conditions and good cultural practices.

productivity
resistance to disease
resistance to lodging
drought-tolerance
good response to fertiliser
Weak points
high shattering
hairy grain
behaviour when cooked.

IRAT 112: Origin: selected in Ivory Coast, descended from a cross between IRAT 13 and Dourado Precoce.
Average yield: 2.2 t/ha
Maximum yield: 4.5 t/ha
Period from sowing to heading: 75 days
Growth cycle: 100 days
Height: 100 cm
Strong points
grain quality
earliness
resistance to disease
resistance to lodging
Weak points
limited productivity (compared with IRAT 13).

7 Advantages and disadvantages of different cultivation techniques

Cultivation techniques will be considered from the angle of fixed agriculture, with the emphasis on intensification by the use of improved varieties, fertilisers, herbicides and mechanization.

The cultural practices employed are determined, primarily, by the type of mechanization adopted. A number of alternatives are possible:

(a) manual cultivation
Although very time-consuming, it does not require a high level of technical expertise. It is well known to smallholders, by whom it is mastered perfectly.

(b) draught animals
Traction is provided by a pair of animals (zebus or N'Dama cattle in Africa). An important feature of using draught animals is the possibility of additional fertilisation from the animal excrement.

(c) cultivation with small ('garden') tractors or 'adapted' machinery
This category covers equipment with a low output (5 to 30 hp DIN).

(d) conventional mechanized cultivation
This is very similar to that practised in more developed rice-growing areas. Here tractors of more than 25 hp DIN are used.

Mechanization offers various advantages:
- it enables the area cultivated by one person to be increased;
- it increases production per hectare, as cultivations can be of a higher quality;
- it reduces the amount of labour required for a given operation, this enables farmers to devote themselves to other tasks.

In deciding which method to use, each situation must be looked at individually. Consideration must be given to:
(i) what the smallholder can afford; it has been calculated that, in tropical regions for investment in a higher degree of mechanization to

be economically worthwhile, the smallholder must have the following amount of land:

3 to 5 hectares for draught animals;

6 to 12 hectares for small-scale mechanization.

50 to 100 hectares for conventional mechanization.

(ii) the size and shape of the plots;

(iii) the farmer's technical expertise (agricultural, animal husbandry, mechanical, etc.);

(iv) the existence of an adequate infrastructure for maintaining the equipment, supplying the fuel, spare parts, etc.

The more complicated the equipment, the more acute these constraints are. Conventional mechanized cultivation calls for considerable technical knowledge. The equipment if expensive, sometimes breaks easily and operating it is a delicate matter, which means that it is recommended only in very specific cases. Therefore in this handbook the emphasis will be placed on draught animals and adapted mechanization.

Solutions combining a number of types of mechanization are traditionally used. Thus, land preparation, sowing and transporting the harvest may be carried out by draught animals, the other operations being done by hand.

Alternatively, only land clearance, improvement and preparation of the soil may be mechanized, other operations remaining manual.

The use of draught animals combined with mechanized cultivation is, encountered more rarely but could be of interest in certain countries, such as Mali, Upper Volta, Senegal and northern Ivory Coast.

It is important to bear in mind that any innovation may cause changes to other areas involved in growing a cropping time taken to do a job, area cultivated, timetable of cultural operations, income, etc.) and gives rise to new problems.

For example, while the use of herbicides admittedly eases the labour bottleneck encountered with the manual weeding of rice, the smallholder then tends to increase the area cultivated, although the labour available will not enable him to cope with a bigger harvest (in terms of the volume and the time taken).

If one problem is not to be replaced by another, the cultivation techniques and way in which they are combined must be carefully thought out and each operation considered individually. The smallholder should therefore be able, throughout the growth cycles of the different crops, to cope with the workload involved with the area cultivated and the rotations, without there being any idle periods.

8 Upland rice crop rotations

An economic way of maintaining soil fertility at a suitable level and controlling weeds is to include rice as part of a crop rotation system. These two aspects make it a priority to promote crop rotation as a cultivation technique.

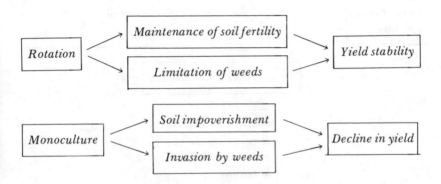

There are a wide range of possible rotations. In making a choice, the farmer must, however, be guided by a number of important points:-
(i) the worst crop to precede upland rice is rice itself;
(ii) the best crops to precede rice are those which are generally good for cereals, i.e., legumes, such as groundnuts, cowpeas, and soya beans, which enrich the soil with nitrogen, and green manure;
(iii) rice, is itself a fairly poor predecessor for other crops, particularly for sorghum.

The choice of which crops to grow in succession generally depends on the balance that is to be achieved between satisfying the smallholders' food requirements and the economic attraction of cash crops in terms of the high monetary income. For example, in certain regions of Senegal, groundnuts, which are an excellent predecessor for upland rice, and the cultivation of which is strongly encouraged by the attractive prices and the well-organized marketing, is found in all rotations.

In most cases, the length of the fallow period depends on demographic pressure. Land used to be left fallow for long periods (ten years or more) but the period is tending to be reduced, which is very harmful.

In agricultural terms, of the crops which traditionally precede upland rice in West Africa, legumes such as cowpeas, soya beans and groundnuts, and cleaning crops such as cotton and maize are regarded as good predecessors.

Sorghum, rice and fallows (particularly short-term) are, however, fairly poor predecessors.

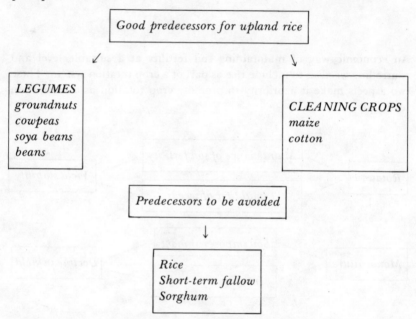

The degree of complexity of the rotation depends on rainfall and whether this allows having one or two cropping seasons in the same year. In the event of two rainy seasons, it is necessary to determine whether the first or the second is best suited for rice, depending on the environment in question.

Examples of crop rotations in different regions

Region with 1 000 to 1 400 mm of rain in one crop season

Year	Crops
1	Yams and Maize and Sorgham
2	Cotton
3	Groundnuts Sorghum
4	Upland rice
5	Fallow

or

Year	Crop
1	Maize
2	Cotton
3	Upland rice
4	Groundnuts

Region with 1000 to 1400 mm of rain in two crop seasons

Year	Season	Crop
1	1	
	2	Yams
2	1	Maize
	2	Cotton
3		Rice
4	1	Maize
	2	Cotton
5		Rice

or

Year	Season	Crop
1		Rice
2	1	Maize
	2	Soya or groundnuts
3		Rice
4	1	Maize
	2	Cotton

9 Land preparation

The first operation is to clear the land of all stumps, roots etc to allow for the use of machinery such as ploughs.

There are many reasons for land preparation, the most important of which are:

(i) **to put the surface of the land into such a condition that a seeder may be used,**

Fig 23 *Preparing the soil by hand*

(ii) **to control weeds**
(iii) **to improve the chemical characteristics of the soil**
    by incorporating various types of fertilizers, minerals and organic
    matter
(iv) **to improve the physical characteristics**
    so as to encourage germination of the seed and root development.

A number of operations may be necessary to bring the soil to the required standard. It is advised that the following be carried out:
- deep ploughing with or without turning over the soil,
- surface work involving breaking up the seedbed, and, in some cases, if there are too many bumps or depressions, rolling in order to firm up the ground.

Manual cultivation will not be dealt with in this chapter, as this kind of soil preparation is fairly limited, and is generally confined to a light hoeing with an instrument such as the 'daba', which only moves the surface layer. Usually, the smallholder is well practised in this technique.

Ploughing

Except in special cases, ploughing would appear to be desirable from the agricultural point of view:
- the extent to which the soil is loosened by ploughing, even at a limited depth, is greater than that achieved by using equipment with tines which do not turn the soil over;

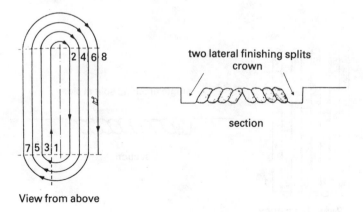

two lateral finishing splits
crown

section

View from above

Fig 24 *Bedding by roundabout ploughing starting at the centre: gathering*

- the burying of straw, manure and other compost is possible with ploughing;
- the control of weeds is also much easier and more complete following deep working and turning over of the soil.

Ploughing begs the question of the type of traction. This can be done using draught animals or tractors. Whatever is used, it will be an enormous change after manual cultivation and will involve considerable expenditure. Thus, ploughing must be advised with care. If it is not done properly and at the right time, it may have disastrous consequences,

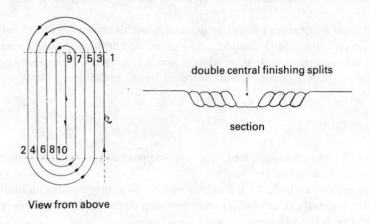

Fig 25   *Bedding by roundabout ploughing starting at the outside: casting*

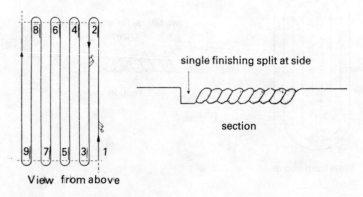

Fig 26   *One-way ploughing*

particularly where there are steep stopes or soils which are susceptible to erosion (even if they are improved) or in areas with a high rainfall and very hard climate.

It should be emphasized that if maximum benefit is to be obtained from ploughing it must be combined with other intensive techniques e.g., rotation, fertilisation, weeding.

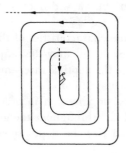

Fig 27   *Round and round ploughing*

Different types of ploughing

There are three basic methods of ploughing, which depend primarily on the type of plough used or, on specific constraints. If the smallholder has a non-reversible plough, the method employed will be:

either **(i) ploughing in beds**
The plough will always push the earth to the same side in relation to the direction of travel and the side on which the soil will be inverted will therefore change with each 180° turn made at the end of the furrow (see diagram);

or **(ii) 'round-and-round' ploughing**
This consists of going round the field starting either from the centre or from one side and enables ploughing comparable to one-way ploughing to be achieved, even though the plough is not reversible.

(iii) one-way ploughing
If the smallholder has a reversible plough, he will undertaken this. The earth will always be pushed to the same side of the field, i.e., the plough will invert the soil alternately to the right and the left by going up and down the field and making adjacent furrows.

Ploughing characteristics

Width and depth

The action of ploughing turns over a continuous slice of earth. The width of that slice depends on the width of the plough-share, which is itself limited by the power available for traction: using oxen, the plough-share seldom exceeds ten inches (25 cm) wide; using tractors, the width is usually twelve or fourteen inches (30–35 cm) but a width of sixteen inches is possible.

The depth is also determined by the characteristics of the plough and the tractive force, but to some extent it may be adjusted by the ploughman: with animal-drawn tillage the depth is rarely more than 10 to 15 cm, with tractors it may be as much as 30 cm.

Unbroken set-up furrow slices must be aimed at in order to bury the weeds and create porosity which will last throughout the growth cycle to encourage good rooting. With upland rice the depth should preferably exceed 20 cm.

Deep ploughing ⟶	*Effective ploughing*

When to plough

The timing of ploughing is particularly important. Two periods are possible: *at the start of the crop cycle* or at the *end of the cycle*.
Ploughing may be undertaken at the beginning of the cycle as soon as the first rains have sufficiently moistened the soil. Two or three showers of 20 mm are generally necessary for first-class work. After 40 mm of rain, two days are generally needed for the soil to dry out so that it is possible to get on to the land easily.

The appropriate ploughing time is generally very short with upland crops as this is often a busy time of year for the farmer. *Nevertheless it is essential not to be late, for if sowing is postponed it will have a disastrous effect on yields.* Good ploughing takes a long time to do, a (5 to 6 days/ha with draught animals, 1 day/ha with tractors). If the farmer is short of time to ensure that the work is of a reasonable standard (which is a prerequisite for effective ploughing), it is better, either to bring forward some of the ploughing to the end of the preceding cycle, or to replace ploughing, on certain plots, with another, faster type of cultivation (e.g., 'reduced tillage') rather than to impede the progress of the crop cycle.

End-of-cycle ploughing is undertaken after the rainy season crop has been harvested and before the soil dries out or becomes hard, this happens at the beginning of the dry season and then precludes any form of deep ploughing. This time may also coincide with a heavy demand on labour for other things e.g., harvesting of other crops, treatment of cotton plants, etc. which may prevent ploughing from being carried out properly.

It should be noted that end-of-cycle ploughing is not possible with all crop rotations, particularly if the plant's growth cycle extends into the dry season, as is the case with cotton plants and traditional cereals (late varieties of millet and sorghum), which are harvested after the rains have stopped.

Furthermore, on soils which are very susceptible to erosion, end-of-cycle ploughing must be avoided if it means the soil is left bare for too long.

Direction of ploughing
Upland rice is often grown on sloping ground where there is a high risk of erosion.

Therefore it is imperative that ploughing always be done perpendicular to the steepest gradient and parallel to the contour lines.

To reduce erosion $\longrightarrow$	*Plough along the contour lines*

Fig 28   *Ploughing with draught animals*

41

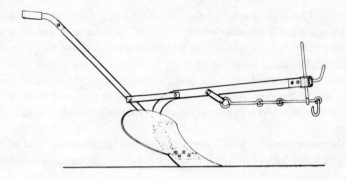

Fig 29 *Plough without stabilizers*

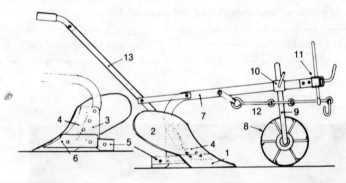

1 share	2 mouldboard	3 + 4 frog	5 landside heel
6 landside	7 beam	8 supporting wheel	9 wheel upright
10 adjustable yoke	11 hake bar	12 hake chain	13 handles

Fig 30 *Plough with longitudinal stabilization*

Equipment

Ploughing with draught animals

The choice is between simple ploughs and more versatile machinery ('multicultivators', 'polycultivators')*, which, with certain adjustments, can be used for a number of operations in turn.

* A definition of the equipment referred to in this chapter is given in the glossary.

The latter type of equipment has been considerably developed, particularly for animal-drawn tillage because of the flexibility it offers. However the work done is often somewhat inferior to that performed by a simple plough.

For ploughing proper, six-inch (15 cm) ploughs are generally used, the ploughing being done in beds.

Ploughing with adapted motorized equipment

There are many types of equipment and they are steadily increasing in number:

motorized cultivators of 5 to 12 hp DIN,

small 15 to 30 hp DIN tractors (Bouyer, Fiat, Pangolin, Tinkabi, etc.).

Ploughing may be done in beds or one-way. Various implements may be used:

The mouldboard plough (12-inch single-furrow, 10-inch two-furrow), whose main advantage is the first-class way it inverts the soil and buries crop residues, etc., but which is difficult to adjust. The single-furrow plough is preferred where the ground is very hard, otherwise the two-furrow plough may be used because it is faster.

Fig 31 *Ploughing with conventional motorized equipment*

The disc plough, whose advantages compared with the mouldboard plough are that it can be used even in areas which have not been properly cleared, at a faster speed and with less rapid wear. However, it is often misused, which may have a disastrous effect.

Ploughing with conventional motorized equipment
A large range of tractors with an output of more than 30 hp DIN is currently available. A two or three furrow mouldboard or disc plough may be used with these tractors, depending on the tractive power available.

It should be noted that all these operations require a good knowledge of the equipment. A badly adjusted plough will prevent the desired work from being done and consume more power than necessary.

Carefully adjust the plough prior to ploughing

Reduced tillage with tined equipment: an alternative solution

Working with tined equipment is not ploughing but it does have certain characteristics in common; that is why people often speak of 'pseudo-ploughing'.

Generally speaking, tined equipment is used only to complete the work done with the plough, i.e., for loosening the soil and destroying weeds, but it may usefully replace ploughing:
(a) where the farmer is in a hurry, in particular if he is late or if there have been irregularities in the rainy season which have upset the crop timetable and caused operations to overlap. The speed at which this type of equipment can work (1.5 to 2 days/ha with animal-drawn tillage; 1 to 3 hours/ha with tractors) permits satisfactory minimum preparation of the topsoil;
(b) where the top soil is shallow, covering a sterile or gravelly layer which traditional ploughing would bring to the surface.   However, reduced tillage with tined implements is of little use insofar as controlling weeds is concerned.

Working with draught animals

It is possible to work with:
- swing ploughs, which are used primarily in arid regions and which

44

plough furrows with slightly raised edges (Planta swing plough, Knoll swing plough, etc.).

– cultivators, which are increasingly replacing swing ploughs: these are implements with rigid or spring tines, the tips of which ('shares') may vary in shape.

Of the different models of cultivator the most commonly used at present is the 'Canadian' (a cultivator with three to five flat spring tines). On very hard ground, two passes are sometimes recommended. The second must be at right angles to the first so as to do a good job and produce a rut-fee surface.

Reduced-tillage with two-wheeled tractors

The implements are similar to those used with animal-drawn tillage. The only difference is that the work can be done more quickly. Depending on the condition and the type of soil, it is possible to attach to the two-wheeled tractor a five to seventined Canadian cultivator.

Reduced tillage with conventional tractors

There is a wider range of implements available but knowing how to use them is can be difficult:

(i)   chisel ploughs, which require a high output (15 to 20 hp/tine) to work deep. If the soil is too wet it will not break up. Conversely, where the soil is too dry or over-compacted it will be difficult for the chisel plough to pass through the it. The use of the chisel plough is justified at the end of a crop cycle;

(ii) tillers, which are used in preference to the chisel plough where the land has not been properly cleared or in the case of very stony soils;

(iii) spring-tined cultivators, which, like tillers, can operate with a wide sweep if considerable tractive power is available.

Reduced tillage with discs

Implements with discs are inappropriate for draught animals as they are generally heavy pieces of equipment which require considerable tractive effort and which work well only at high speeds, only possible with tractors; besides, they are very expensive.

For motorized cultivation, such implements are available as part of the range of machinery that can be adapted to fit multi-purpose bodies. However, their use is ruled out in cases where there is a high risk of erosion (they crumble up the soil into very fine particles) or where there are weeds with rhizomes, which they fragment and cause to spread. Their value is therefore debatable.

Risk of erosion?	⟶	*Avoid implements with discs*

Secondary tillage of ploughed land

The main aim of surface cultivation is to prepare the seedbed so that the seeds germinate properly.

The seedbed must possess certain characteristics: *moisture*, so as to enable the seeds to swell up and the seedlings to emerge; in terms of *structure*, the soil must be loose with aggregates of medium size; in order to avoid the risks of erosion and surface capping if the tilth is too fine, the largest clods may be as big as a man's fist; the rain will subsequently break up the clods giving the desired structure.

In order to obtain a regular surface, it is advised that the soil be worked down at right angles to the direction of ploughing. Furthermore, in order to prevent weed growth, care must be taken to ensure that the land is worked down only a short while prior to sowing.

Ideal conditions for sowing	⟶	*Moist ground* *Soil loose but not puffed up* *Seedbed fairly coarse* *Clean soil*

Secondary tillage with draught animals

The work may be done with:
- multicultivators equipped with Canadian-type tines or with rigid tines complete with shares (scarifiers);
- harrows, which give good results, particularly on wet soils after they have dried out. The best work is done on friable soils. It is quicker to use a harrow rather than the Canadian cultivator but the former produces a finer tilth and therefore increases the risk of erosion.

Where sowing is to be done by hand it is not really necessary to rework the soil. However, if a seeder is to be used after ploughing, harrowing is useful, particularly with animal-drawn tillage, as seeders are light and very sensitive to jolting over irregular surfaces.

Secondary tillage with small tractors

The same range of tools is available as before: a Canadian cultivator, a spring-tined cultivator or a harrow can be fitted to a tractor unit.

Normally, it is best not to make too many passes, so as to reduce the risk of compaction and prevent deterioration of the soil structure. Sometimes, just one pass with the plough is enough.

Secondary tillage with conventional tractors

The equipment referred to in the case of small tractors can be used with conventional tractors.

The items of equipment described here do not compete with one another but are complementary, each giving good results under particular conditions which we have endeavoured to describe in detail. It is therefore not possible to recommend just one particular type of equipment.

It should be borne in mind that mechanization does not automatically provide a solution to all problems. It requires an appropriate level of technical skill and also a commensurate technical and economic environment without which it may prove to be harmful rather than profitable.

10 Fertilising

Rice is extremely sensitive to the amount and balance of nutrients in the soil.

What are the principal nutrients required?

As with most crops, the chief nutrients required are nitrogen, phosphorus and potassium.

NITROGEN – Nitrogen has a crucial role to play in obtaining higher yields.
It encourages tillering and plant growth. If sufficient quantities of nitrogen are not present in the soil, the plant remains small with only a few tillers. Also the leaves, which sometimes become brittle, show a characteristic yellowing.

PHOSPHORUS - Phosphorus also encourages growth in rice, particularly of the root system. It has a favourable effect on earliness. Where phosphorus is deficient, the leaves become dark green or purplishgreen, with yellow spots between the veins. Their tips turn red.

POTASSIUM - Potassium enables water to be saved up in the tissues confers some resistance to lodging and increases resistance to disease. It also increases the size and weight of the grain. Potassium deficiency is reflected in poor tillering and yellowing of the tips of older leaves and of the central vein.

The absence of one of these three elements gives rise to abnormal plant growth and to a substantial reduction in yields. Abbreviations are frequently used to represent the three main nutrients: N for nitrogen; P for phosphorus; and K for potassium. Other less important elements may, however, have an effect on growth and yields, e.g.:- sulphur, calcium, magnesium and iron.

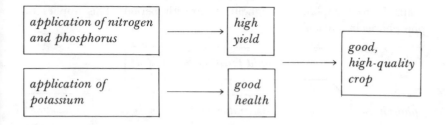

Different types of fertiliser

According to their nitrogen, phosphorus and potassium content, a distinction is made between:

(i) straight fertilisers
These are chemical substances which supply only one of the main three elements:
  urea or ammonium sulphate provides nitrogen,
  superphosphates provide phosphorus,
  potassium chloride provides potassium.
These fertilisers do not supply the elements in their pure state and this should be taken into account when calculating doses that are to be applied:- thus urea contains 46% nitrogen, i.e., in 100 kg of urea there is only 46 kg of nitrogen. Thus, if you wish to apply 30 kg of nitrogen, you must in fact use:

$$\frac{30}{0.46} = 65 \text{ kg of urea.}$$

(ii) compound fertilisers
These provide two or three of the main elements together. They are 'binary' if they contain only two compounds and 'ternary' if there are three, in which case one also speaks of 'complete' fertilisers. They are usually characterized by their formulation, which defines the respective proportions of each element.

Generally, in these formulations the first figure corresponds to nitrogen, the second to phosphorus and the third to potassium; in fact, the phosphorus content is usually indicated in the form of the P_2O_5 content and the potassium content in the form of the K_2O content. For instance, 10-18-18, a complete fertiliser, is a ternary fertiliser containing, per 100 kg of product:
  10 kg or units of nitrogen,
  18 units of phosphorus, or to be more precise, 18 units of P_2O_5,
  18 units of potassium, i.e., 18 units of K_2O.

Some fertilisers may be applied prior to sowing and will then be available to the plant throughout its growth period. This applies to phosphorus in particular.

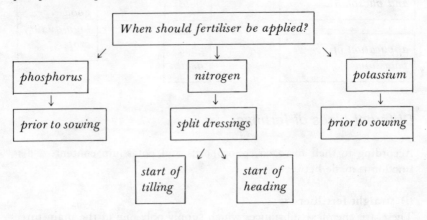

Other fertilisers may easily leach away or be so volatile that they must be applied a number of times during the growth of the plant. This applies to nitrogen in particular.

It is important to note that nitrogenous fertiliser should be applied 'on demand'. The plant needs nitrogen when it is tillering and from the 'booting' stage to the end of ripening. It may, however, be slightly lacking in nitrogen at the end of tillering, prior to booting; this may cause a reduction in vegetative growth.

Splitting the nitrogen dressing will enable the plant to tiller well (fertilising at the start of tillering) and the grains to fill out well (fertilising at booting).

What quantities should be applied?

The amount of mineral elements applied to a crop depend on many factors:

(a) the requirements specific to the plant, which govern the relative proportion of elements required (nitrogen, phosphorus or potassium) in order to ensure growth.

   In order to give an idea of the order of magnitude, the table below shows the quantity of elements consumed to produce a tonne of paddy.

(b) the level of intensification aimed at (1 t, 2 t, 3 t/ha or more, etc.), which then determines the level at which the fertiliser should be applied. This depends on the variety planted and on the risk of drought.

   The effectiveness of mineral fertilisation is also related to the use

Amount required to produce a tonne of paddy	Uptake complete plant*	Removed panicle alone
N	24	13
P_2O_5	12	7
K_2O	34	4

in kg/ha   (source: Senegal)

of other crop improving techniques; there is little point in applying large amounts of expensive fertiliser if weeding has not been properly carried out.

(c) the amounts of each element provided by the soil. This depends upon the volume of earth into which the roots extend and the chemical composition of the soil. It may happen that, right from the start the soil will be lacking in certain elements. (Experience shows that in many cases soils are deficient in phosphorus.) Such a deficiency must be corrected by adequate fertilisation.

After harvesting, before any other operation is carried out it is important to restore to the soil the elements removed by the crop. Obviously, less routine fertilisation will be needed if crop residues are ploughed back into the soil or burnt.

In particular, these practices make it possible to cut down on the amount of potassium fertiliser. The extent of the savings made is shown in the table, which compares the uptake by the whole plant (straw and grains) with that by the panicle alone.

Returning crop residues to the soil is beneficial

(d) the losses caused by leaching of these elements by drainage water and run-off or by evaporation into the atmosphere. The traditional nitrogenous fertilisers are particularly soluble and therefore susceptible to leaching by rainwater. It is therefore important to split dressings in order to limit losses.

In order to avoid breaking into the fertility reserves of the soil, routine fertiliser applications should offset:

uptake of elements by the whole plant and the losses if the crop residues are not returned to the soil;

uptake of elements by the grains alone, plus the losses, if the nutrients are not returned to the soil.

fertiliser applications = elements + elements + losses
removed in   removed in
straw   grain

To sum up the different types of application possible, a distinction may be made between:
- **the application needed to correct certain deficiencies** (in particular phosphorus) **or certain toxicities** (acidity of the soil) This correction will be done prior to sowing, the additional substances (fertiliser, phosphates, magnesium, limestone) being ploughed in.
- **routine fertiliser**, normally based on nitrogen, phosphorus and potassium, which may be applied either as a basic dressing prior to ploughing or as a top dressing (as is the case with nitrogen);
- **the application required to correct other deficiencies** (e.g., zinc), which is given as a top dressing.

INCREASE THE EFFECTIVENESS OF YOUR FERTILISERS!
Prepare your soil carefully.
Use modern varieties which respond well to fertilisers.
Apply the appropriate dose at the right time.
Choose a time when there is no dew or risk of rain.
Do not let weeds benefit from the fertiliser instead
of the rice: weed BEFORE applying fertiliser rather
than afterwards.

General recommendations for each country have been made by the relevant research institutes. The doses to be applied do, however, vary quite considerably according to the local situations. It is therefore recommended that the development agencies be consulted in order to examine with them which formula is best suited to each case.

By way of example, we give here some formulas recommended by IRAT for different African countries (see table below). This is for routine fertilising, without taking account of any correction for deficiencies or toxicities.

These figures are for fertilising soils cultivated under a system of continuous rotational cropping, the crop residues being returned to the land. The recommended doses do not include the routine liming that is necessary with tropical soils, which soon become acid if cultivated intensively.

These formulas are the optimum rates of application to be aimed at. In practice, the cost per unit of fertiliser compared with the selling price per

Routine fertilising of upland rice according to level of intensification aimed at

	Traditional cultivation	Semi-intensive cultivation	Intensive cultivation
Ivory Coast	100 kg of 10.18.18 prior to sowing 50 kg of urea at booting	200 kg of 10.18.18 prior to sowing 100 kg of urea at booting	300 kg of 10.18.18 prior to sowing 150 kg of urea at booting
Upper Volta	100 kg of 14.23.14 prior to sowing 50 kg of urea at tillering	100 kg of 14.23.14 prior to sowing 50 kg of potassium chloride prior to sowing 100 kg of urea at tillering	
Senegal	100 kg of 8.12.27 prior to sowing 50 kg of urea at tillering	150 kg of 8.12.27 prior to sowing 100 kg of urea at tillering	250 kg of 8.12.27 prior to sowing 200 kg of urea at tillering

kg of crop is the crucial element governing fertiliser application by small farmers. Unfortunately, this relationship is often unfavourable in West Africa (although varying according to the country concerned and its policy on this matter). Nevertheless, intensive cultivation cannot be carried out unless the minerals removed from the soil are put back either through crop residues, organic fertiliser or artificial fertiliser.

Fertilising techniques

Spreading fertiliser

Two methods are possible:
(i) manual spreading, which can be done by broadcasting or by distributing the fertiliser along the rows, according to how the sowing was undertaken and the stage at which the fertiliser is applied;

53

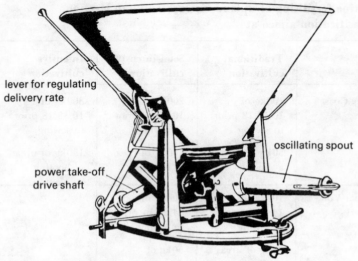

lever for regulating
delivery rate

oscillating spout

power take-off
drive shaft

Fig 32 *Centrifugal fertiliser distributor with oscillating spout (CEEMAT drawing adapted from Vicon)*

(ii) mechanical spreading (only with mechanized cultivation) with centrifugal distributors. For this type of equipment to be used, there must be a minimum gap between the rows.

Incorporation of crop residues

The incorporation of crop residues makes it possible to limit the amounts of elements removed from the soil (see table).

The method of harvesting effects the way in which crop residues are buried. In some cases, the straw will be left in a homogeneous mass on the soil; in other cases, the straw will have been gathered together for drying; it has to be uniformly redistributed prior to being buried.

Normally, burial is carried out directly by ploughing in, which is only possible with mechanized cultivation (i.e., where draught animals or tractors are used). It is also possible burn the residues (this is the traditional procedure), or to have them grazed by livestock. The animal dung must then be incorporated into the soil either at the stage of rotary crushing or of stubble ploughing with discs prior, to ploughing in proper.

Particular problems of tropical soils

Acidity

The phenomenon of soils becoming acid is very widespread. Moreover, intensive cultivation and the repeated use of fertilisers contribute towards accentuating this process. Thus the use of carbonate of lime or magnesian limestone to correct the balance must become a routine operation. This type of soil improvement is already practised with success by some African farmers.

A number of methods may be considered for correcting and raising the pH if it falls below 5.8: either apply 150 to 200 kg of magnesian limestone per annum or 400 to 500 kg every three years; or, if the situation is serious, apply a large amount (of the order of 1 to 4 tonnes/ha).

Subsequently, losses will be offset by regular annual applications. Whatever dose is decided upon, the product should be spread prior to ploughing or any other preparatory cultivation.

Mineral toxicity phenomena, which are often related to acidity, are difficult to correct.

Deficiencies

Mineral deficiencies are difficult to identify, as the symptoms are very similar, but they are easily remedied by simply applying the deficient element, provided, however, that the yield increase obtained will cover the cost of correcting the deficiency.

Phosphorus deficiency

This type of deficiency is very widespread in West Africa. It can be remedied at a relatively low cost by using the natural deposits in the region.

The dose generally recommended for correcting the deficiency is of the order of 400 kg/ha of tricalcium phosphate applied as a basic dressing after land clearance and preparatory cultivation, the rate to be adjusted of course, according to the natural richness of the land.

Subsequently, the level thus obtained will be maintained by the phosphate included in the routine fertilising. However, it may be necessary after a few years of intensive cultivation to repeat the operation.

Zinc deficiency

Under certain chalky soil conditions, the plants may show signs of zinc deficiency (ferruginous brown spots on the tissues on either side of the veins of the mature leaves). Here, a top dressing of 20 kg of zinc sulphate generally solves the problem.

Techniques for reducing the amount of artificial fertiliser

Certain techniques make it possible to reduce to some extent, the amount of artificial fertiliser used. Given the cost of fertiliser in West Africa, these are to be encouraged.

The most effective techniques include:

(i) the systematic introduction of legumes as part of the rotation
Cowpeas, soya beans, groundnuts, etc., may reduce the artificial nitrogenous fertiliser requirement for the following crop;

(ii) the application, as frequently as possible, of organic fertiliser
Based on **dung** and **compost**, which have the merit of improving the
structure of the soil. These two techniques are particularly recommended.
Mention may also be made of **working the soil**: properly done, it
encourages good rooting of the seedlings and satisfactory covering of the
soil, reducing run-off and erosion; it also permits better uptake by the crop
of the nutrients present in the soil.

Rotation with legumes	
Erosion control	
Application of manure ⟶	*Savings on*
Incorporation of crop residues	*artificial fertilisers*
Careful and early weeding	

11 Sowing

What to sow

It is recommended that 'certified' seeds supplied by development agencies should be used. If this is not possible, the farmer may select the best seeds from his preceding harvest, eliminating those which are small, empty or broken.

In order to stop seed from rotting in the soil or from being devoured by pests, it is a good idea to treat it beforehand with a mixture of fungicides and insecticides.

So that the seed is properly coated by the product, the powder and the seed are put into a 100-litre drum and carefully stirred. In order to ensure perfect mixing, small quantities should be treated at a time (batches of 20-25 kg). If a drill is used for sowing, mixing may be done directly in the drill hopper.

Active ingredient (a.i.)	Commercial product (c.p.) (in form of powder)	Dosage (commercial product)
Thiram + heptachlor	Thioral	300 g of c.p./10 kg of seed
Captafol + lindane	Capta Granox	300 g of c.p./10 kg
Carbendazim + benomyl + carbofuran	Granox	200 g of c.p./10 kg

N.B.: these products are dangerous and render the treated seed totally unfit for human or animal consumption.

When to sow

The date of sowing must be worked out according to the water requirements of the rice. The period when the water requirement is greatest (usually twenty days before flowering to twenty days after) must correspond to the time when the maximum rainfall is expected.

If the date when it is preferable that heading should take place and the length of the period between sowing and heading of each variety are known (data given in Chapter 5 'The rice plant' the optimum sowing date may be determined for each variety.)

There is, however, some leeway either side of this date, generally a week before to a week after. To put it more simply, sowing must take place after the start of the rainy season in order to ensure that the soil contains the minimum amount of moisture necessary for germination of the seed, but not too long after. Traditionally, the sowing was often done some time after the start of the rainy season, as this was a fairly busy time of year for the farmer; however, it is imperative to sow early for the crop to succeed. **Sowing late results in a fall in yield proportional to how late the seed is sown.**

> *The later seed is sown, the poorer the yield.*
>
> *observe the crop calendar: sow when the first rains fall.*

In some African countries, particularly Senegal, the seed is sown not on wet, but on dry soil. This practice has the advantage, to some extent of solving the problems brought about by a congested crop calendar. This is extremely risky as it presupposes that it is virtually certain that there will be rain in the days following sowing. It should therefore be reserved strictly for areas where the rainy season starts very regularly on the same date.

How to sow

A number of general principles should be observed, whichever method of sowing is used:

(i) the best depth of sowing for good emergence is between 1 and 4 cm
Sowing closer to the surface of the soil (1 to 3 cm) is to be preferred if one can be certain that the soil will remain moist during germination;

> THE DEPTH OF SOWING IS CRUCIAL FOR GOOD EMERGENCE

(ii) the seed must be in good contact with the soil
The soil must be loose for the roots to develop. Also, slight firming of the earth over the seed is generally beneficial. Care must, however, be taken to prevent of the formation of a crust, which will inhibit the emergence of the seedlings;

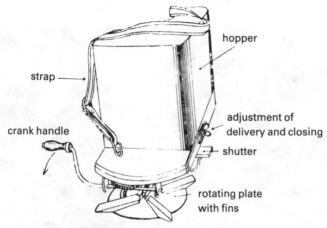

Fig 33 *Centrifugal seed broadcaster (can also be used for granulated fertiliser)*
[Drawing CEEMAT]

(iii) seeds must be sown parallel
in order to avoid erosion, to the contour lines. Sowing density, spacing of
the seeds, the equipment to be used and the time required to carry out the
operation vary according to the method of sowing employed.

Dibbling

This is one of the traditional techniques used in the case of manual
cultivation. Dibbling is a very simple operation to perform correctly and
and may be used anywhere, whatever the state of the soil (poorly cleared of
roots and stumps, stony, etc.). The seeds are sown seven or eight at a time
in a hole four or five cm deep, dug with a pointed implement or a stick.
The planter covers the seedhole with earth and then firms it with his foot.

  In practice, the spacing between seedholes varies between ten and forty
cm. Sowing density rarely exceeds 30 to 35 kg/ha.

  This type of sowing takes five to ten days per hectare.

Broadcasting

Broadcasting of seed may be done either manually or using a seeder Once
this operation is completed, the seeds must be buried by harrowing or
dragging branches over the ground. This is seldom done with traditional
upland rice cultivation, because it often leads to poor germination.
Therefore, in order to make up for this poor emergence of the seedlings,
the amount of seed sown is fairly high: it may be as much as or more than
100 kg/ha, whereas it could be slightly reduced if the seed were covered (80
to 90 kg/h would then be enough).

59

Fig 34   *Dibbling*

Broadcasting is fairly fast (between two and five days per hectare Even if the sower is skilled and the distribution is even, this practice makes weeding by hand difficult and mechanical hoeing impossible. That is the main drawback of this method, which should therefore be reserved for areas without major weed problems (e.g., where the land has recently been cleared, etc.) or areas where the use of herbicides is possible.

Drilling

Done completely by hand, this is both a very long and very laborious task. Thus, most of the time it is done using a seed-drill. There are drill systems for all types of traction (manual, animal, motorized), consisting of devices for distributing, burying and covering the seeds, which can sow one or more rows at a time.

Compared with other methods of sowing, the advantages of drilling are:

(i) the time saving: it takes only a few hours to drill a hectare with the motorized system, 1 to 1.5 days with the animal-drawn system and 1.5 to 3 days with the manual traction system;

(ii) the fact that it makes it possible weeding by hand and the use of machinery for mechanical hoeing, spreading of fertiliser or of other dressings, etc.

60

Fig 35 *Manual seed drill*

The amount of seed sown per hectare varies from 40 to 80 kg/ha according to the variety used, the average weight of the grains and the tillering capacity.

For instance, the variety *Dourado Precoce*, which has a fairly low tillering ability, must be sown at a density of 80 kg/ha.

The spacing between rows is governed by the method of weeding chosen, which in each case determines the minimum distance required:

for manual hoeing with a 'daba': 25 to 30 cm;

for animal-drawn or motorized hoeing: 40 to 45 cm at least

is required;

here, the number of rows sown at the same time must be equal to or a multiple of the number of inter-row spaces subsequently weeded.

Yields appear to be hardly affected at all by differences of this order: increasing the distance from 20 to 40 cm leaves the yield virtually unchanged. It may be worth having a wide spacing between rows in areas where the risk of drought is high. This practice is common in Latin

Fig 36   *Manual seed drilling*

America. However, weed control is always better with closer spacing of rows (quicker covering is always better with closer spacing of rows (quicker covering of the soil). A compromise should therefore be sought, depending on local conditions.

In Africa, were crops often err on the side of too low a density to the hectare, it is recommended that seeds be sown more closely together.

Correct spacing ⟶	*Satisfactory tillering* ⟶	*High yield*

Drilling may be done in a special way: the rows may be arranged in pairs, so as to facilitate both mechanical and animal-drawn weeding. Thus, the seed may be sown in double rows 15 cm apart, with a space of 60 cm between each double row.

However, the problem of weeding the narrow space within the double rows has not been resolved, which considerably limits the value of this method.

Fig 37   *Sowing by manual traction*

It is essential that the seed drill is adjusted before being used. In order to do this, pull the drill over a measured distance (at least 10 m) and weigh the seeds which have fallen on the ground. Make sure they are being deposited evenly. If not, adjust the seed rate and repeat the test.

Weight of seed collected over a row	=	Target density	×	Spacing between rows	×	Distance measured
(expressed in g)		(in g/m²)		(expressed in m)		(expressed in m)

Example
Target density = 80 kg/ha, i.e., 80 000 g/10 000 m, or 8 g/m²
Spacing between rows = 0.25 m
Distance selected for measurement = 50 m
Weight of seed collected over a row = 8 × 0.25 × 50 = 100

Fig 38   *Drilled upland rice*

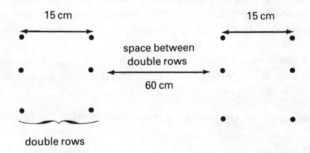

double rows

Fig 39   *Positions of rows*

12 Weeding upland rice

Weeds are one of the main limiting factors in so far as yield is concerned in that they compete directly with the rice for water, light and fertilising elements. Weeding of upland rice is therefore essential. As we have seen in the chapter on major constraints, the problem of weeding arises mainly with regard to fixed cultivation.

Unlike with irrigated cultivation, which benefits from two very effective means of weed control, namely submersion and transplantation, upland rice does not enjoy such advantages. Various procedures may be used, some traditional, involving conventional cultivation techniques, others more recent, consisting of the use of herbicides. The best result is often achieved by using a combination of measures involving different techniques.

Cultivation techniques

There are a number of precautions to which attention should be drawn:
(a) **seed should be sown only in ground which is already clean;**
(b) **it is essential that the weeds growing around the edges of the fields should be eradicated** so that they do not become an additional source of contamination;
(c) lastly, it is important to **sow only seed which has been sorted and which is free of weed seed.** Selected seeds, which are subject to strict controls, are particularly recommended; unfortunately, they are not widely produced.

In so far as cultivation techniques which may facilitate control of weeds are concerned, the following points should be made with regard to:
(i) Land Preparation
The more carefully this is done, the fewer the weeds that appear. In particular, ploughing is important because of its cleaning effect, which is superior to that of superficial tillage.

If a number of cultivations are carried out (e.g., ploughing, followed by two passes with the harrow), it is recommended that the operations be staggered over several days, as the last pass with the harrow will ensure that all the weeds which have germinated in the intervening period are destroyed.

(ii) Rotations:
Rotation may help to control weeds either because certain crops in the rotation require careful weeding or because the specific herbicidal treatment for the preceeding crop destroys weeds which may resist the herbicidal treatment for the rice.

(iii) Method and density of sowing
Rapid and dense coverage of the soil gives the rice an advantage in its competition with weeds. It is therefore better not to sow the seeds too far apart where weed control is regarded as a priority objective.

PRE-CULTIVATION PRECAUTIONS !
Avoid preceding crops which contaminate the soil
(rice, short-term fallow)
Carefully prepare your soil.
Sow only on a clean soil.
Sow only sorted seeds.
Sow close together

LESS WORK DURING CULTIVATION !

Pulling weeds

This refers to weeding by hand, without using any implements. It is impractical, except along rows.

Hoeing

This may be done by hand or mechanically:

Manual hoeing

Manual hoeing is done with tools such as the 'daba'. This is the traditional way of controlling weeds. Its main advantage is its flexibility, as manual weeding may be employed whatever the conditions, even when the soil is very water logged and whichever method of sowing has been used. However, where the seed has been drilled, there must be a gap of at least 20 cm between the rows.

Nevertheless, the procedure is both very laborious and very demanding in terms of labour; up to 300 man-hours per hectare, divided over two or three passes, may be required, depending on when the operation is carried out and the stage of development attained by the weeds. Among smallholders, manual hoeing often constitutes a bottleneck in terms of labour and an obstacle to extending the area cultivated.

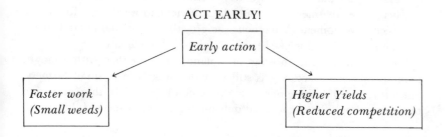

Weeding/hoeing with draught animals

For this type of operation, in order to avoid uprooting the plants it is essential that the seeds have been drilled, that the farmer is technically competent and that the animals are well trained. There must be a gap of at least 40 cm between the rows. This condition is met in particular where the seed has been sown in double rows.

The equipment used is either specific equipment of the 'hoe' type or multi-purpose equipment of the 'multicultivator' type, to which tines with hoe or weeder shares have been fitted.

Only the space between the rows is weeded. This practice does not do away with the initial manual weeding of the rows themselves but later on the rice grows sufficiently to prevent weeds from coming up again in the rows.

The time saving compared with manual hoeing is considerable, as the operation takes one to four days per hectare, according to the type of equipment used (not counting, however, weeding of the rows themselves).

Motorized weeding/hoeing

This solution has the same advantages and drawbacks as the preceding solution, although they are more marked:

(i) even more than in the case of weeding/hoeing with draught animals, this is a high-precision operation, which calls for perfect cleaning of the plot (removal of stumps, roots, etc.) and drilling of the seed with a distance of at least 40 cm between the rows. Moreover, with motorized cultivation or in the case of double rows, the distance between the drills and that between the tines or hoes must be identical.

Generally, the following are used:

- cultivators trailed by the tractor; a second driver sitting on the rear seat can compensate for errors;

- rotary hoes with rigid or flexible tips.

(ii) according to the type of equipment used, weeding takes between three and eight hours per hectare. Combined with a pre-emergence herbicide treatment, it should be sufficient to weed once to control weed development throughout the growth cycle of the upland rice if the product used is persistent enough in a hot climate.

Mechanical weeding/hoeing of upland rice – either with draught animals or using tractors – is still virtuallly unknown to small farmers. Since it is a very delicate operation (precision is essential), this cultivation technique should be encouraged only among the most successful farmers.

Chemical weeding during cultivation

Chemical weeding, which requires only very few man-hours per hectare, has been developed to some extent, although in certain cases the cost of the chemical has been the limiting factor.

Qualities of a good herbicide

It must be effective, selective and persistent:

effective – its effectiveness depends to a large extent on the conditions under which it is applied: it must be applied at the right time, under very specific conditions. Requirements vary according to the herbicide used. These constraints make the application of herbicides a delicate matter.

selective – a selective herbicide destroys weeds, or more precisely, certain weeds, without damaging the crop being grown. Not all herbicides are selective; there are 'total' herbicides, which destroy all plants indiscriminately. These can only be used in between cropping periods.

persistent – it is important for the products to have as long-lasting an action as possible so as to minimize the number of applications. With upland rice, the persistence of the herbicides currently available is barely more than a month but by then the rice may be sufficiently well advanced to no longer suffer from possible competition. Nevertheless, research is under way to develop herbicides with a longer-lasting action.

Timing of application

The timing of the application is generally defined with reference to the growth stage. All situations are possible, as is shown in the table below, so generally both the degree of development of the rice and that of the weeds are specified.

Each herbicide is characterised by its time of application.

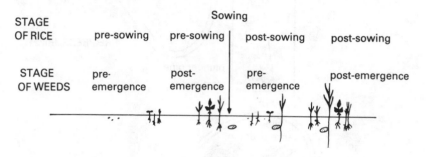

| STAGE OF RICE | pre-sowing | pre-sowing | Sowing | post-sowing | post-sowing |

| STAGE OF WEEDS | pre-emergence | post-emergence | pre-emergence | post-emergence |

Fig 40 *Timing of application of herbicides*

Equipment

Depending on the size of the holding, the farmer's technical ability and financial resources and the formulation of the herbicide, a number of solutions are possible:

> **THREE FORMULATIONS FOR HERBICIDES:**
> - *Absorbent powder* ⎫
> - *Liquid* ⎬ ⟶ *Special equipment*
> - *Granules* ⎭
>   *Granules* ⟶ *No particular equipment*

(i) knapsack sprayers

Either pre-pressurized or under constant pressure; these make it possible to treat a hectare in three or four hours if there are facilities nearby for filling the tank. With conventional sprayers, the quantity of water required varies between 200 and 1 000 litres/ha, which means that water must be available (proximity to a well or 'marigot'). Moreover, the considerable volume to be applied makes the work very tiring. This is why the application of

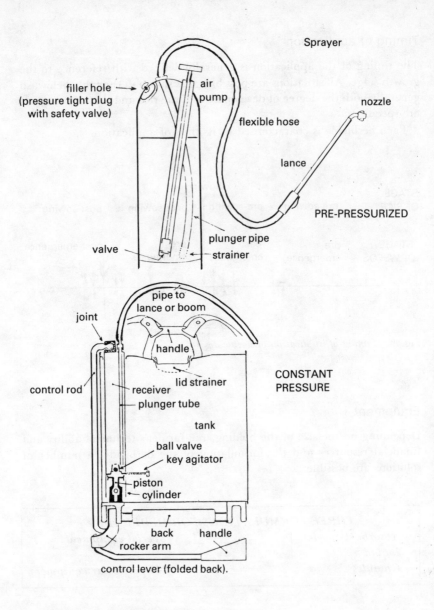

Fig 41 *Pre-pressurized and constant pressure sprayers*

herbicides with this type of equipment has never become particularly widespread among smallholders.

(ii) low-volume spinning-disc sprayers
Because of the low volume used (they require 5 litres of the product plus 15

litres of water, i.e. 20 litres per hectare), they are very attractive to smallholders. They make their work easier, thus explaining the popularity of this type of treatment. NB: not all herbicides may be used in both conventional and low-volume sprayers. This needs to be checked before treatment.

Fig 42 *Knapsack spraying*

(iii) high-output sprayers carried or trailed by a tractor
They have booms between 3 and 12 m wide and are capable of treating several hectares an hour. They require a high level of technical competence and should be recommended only to top-ranking farmers.

Carrying out the treatment

A number of principles may be laid down which are valid in all circumstances:

(i) pre-emergence treatment of rice is more effective if carried out on a wet soil

However, since the principal constraint of this type of treatment is the fact that it must be undertaken before emergence of the rice seedlings, (for reasons of selectivity), or of the weeds (because of the way in which the product acts), it is not always possible to apply the product on a particularly wet soil. Rather than risk a certain degree of phytotoxicity affecting the crop or a loss of effectiveness, it is better to spray just after sowing.

(ii) spraying should be avoided when it is windy

as the product is then unevenly distributed.

(iii) in the event of heavy rainfall

(more than 15 mm) less than six hours after post-emergence treatment of the weeds, **it is sometimes necessary to repeat the operation, as the product is leached away, reducing its effectiveness.** The cost of the repeat treatment is therefore a paramount consideration in deciding whether or not to spray again.

(iv) adjustment of the spraying apparatus is an essential factor in the quality of chemical weeding.

It is necessary to know the quantity of mixture which the apparatus can spread per unit of surface area. That quantity depends on:
- the spraying width.
- the forward speed of the operator.
- the flow rate from the apparatus.

Therefore it is not possible to lay down norms, since each apparatus has its own specific characteristics (nozzle aperture size, state of wear or cleanliness, pump rotation speed, difference in level between the tank and the nozzle for low-volume apparatus, etc.).

Once calibrated, the apparatus must always be used under the same conditions.

Special precautions must be taken by the user when handling a toxic product. It is recommended that he avoid any contact with or ingestion of the product and avoid contaminating wells or other water supplies with the residues from cleaning the sprayers.

Suggested herbicides

The products which may be used for weeding upland rice, classified according to when they should be applied, are grouped together in the following table.

Other herbicides may prove effective under certain specific soil or climatic conditions. Find out about this from the local development agencies.

Examples of herbicide formulations for upland rice as a growing crop (after sowing) for different regions.

Timing of application		Active ingredient	Proprietary name	Dosage of commercial product	Regions
PRE-EMERGENCE OF THE RICE	pre-emergence of the weeds	fluorodifen	REFORAN CE 30	10 l	Senegal
		butraline	MEX 820	4.2 l	Senegal
		oxadiazon	NSTAR CE 250	4 l	Ivory Coast
					Senegal, Brazil, Cameroon
	pre-emergence of the weeds or right at start of weed emergence	thiobencarb	TURN CE 50	4 l	Ivory Coast
		fluorodifen	REFORAN CE 30	5 l	Ivory Coast
		butachlor	ACHETE CE 60	4 l	Ivory Coast
POST-EMERGENCE OF THE RICE	stage 2-3 weed leaves	thiobencarb + propanil	AMARIZ	8 l	Senegal
		propanil + thiobencarb* fenoprop**	AMARIZ SUPER	10 l	West Cameroon, Guyana
	stage 3-4 weed leaves	propanil	STAM F 34	8 l	West Cameroon
		propanil + bentazone	STAM F 34 BASAGRAN PL2	5 to 8 l	Ivory Coast

* formerly benthiocarb
** Fenoprop = 2.4.5.JP

NB: Many experiments are being conducted on rice herbicides and will lead to this list (which was drawn up in 1982) being amended either through the dropping of certain products or the inclusion of new formulations.

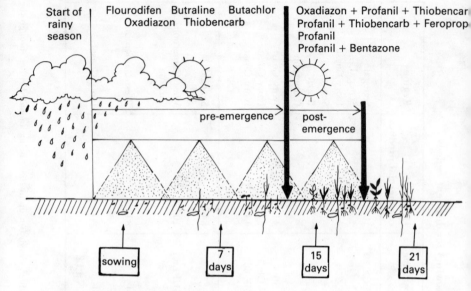

Fig 43 *Times of weeding upland rice*

Chemical weeding between cropping periods

Sometimes the soil is weeded between cropping periods. It is then possible
to use non-selective or 'total' herbicides, which destroy all plants.

Proposed total herbicide formulations between cropping periods

Timing of application	Active ingredient	Propriety name	Dosage of commercial product per hectare
Pre-sowing of the rice	Paraquat	GRAMO-ZONE	2 to 4 l/ha
and post-emergence of the weeds	Glyphosate	ROUND-UP	6 l/ha

In the case of paraquat, it is not necessary to wait for more than a day or
two after treatment before sowing: the product loses its effectiveness upon
contact with the soil and it acts on the weeds very quickly.

In the case of glyphosate, it is usual to wait two or three weeks after treatment before working the soil. Although the product does not present any risk of phytotoxicity for the following crop, it acts very slowly, as the product has to penetrate into the weeds; it must be allowed time to act, particularly if weeds with rhizomes or tubers are to be destroyed (*Imperata, Cyperus,* etc.).

13 Pests affecting upland rice

Insects

Many insects may attack upland rice. The damage they cause is sometimes substantial enough to warrant action by the farmer.

In order to know when and how to treat the crop effectively, it is necessary to know which species one is dealing with and the stage of the rice's development when it is most susceptable. The most damaging pests are the stem borers. These are the Lepidoptera, noctua (*Sesemia*) or pyralis (*Chilo, Maliarpha, Scirpophaga*) or the Diptera (*Diopsides, Ephydrides*).

The life-cycle of these insects is shown below:

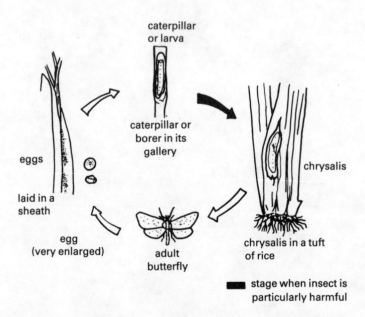

Fig 44 *Life cycle of a typical stem borer*

Fig 45   *White dessicated panicles: borer damage*

They penetrate inside the leaf sheaths and the stems and cause either the death of the young tillering plant or the appearance of white or dessicated panicles without grains.

A member of the *Cecidomyia* family causes distortion of the terminal leaves, which fail to unfurl and extend into a long 'onion leaf-shaped' white tube.

Defoliating insects attack the foliage, which they can completely destroy during tillering: the damage appears suddenly and takes the farmer by surprise, so he often acts too late.

Biting insects attack the grains at the milky stage and may almost completely empty them (bugs). Others eat the foliage (*Cicadidae*) and some may transmit viral diseases (a common phenomenon in Asia).

These insects, and the damage they cause, are described in detail in a brochure entitled 'The Principal insect pests of rice in West Africa and their control', produced by IRAT and published by the ADRAO.

There are a number of ways of combating harmful insects, such as the use of resistant varieties, agricultural control, chemical control and biological control.

Fig 46 *Upland rice stem borers*

Resistant varieties

Some varieties are resistant to borers because of their physical characteristics (thick, woody tissues, rich in silica) or chemical (substances toxic to the insect to a greater or lesser extent).

The use of resistant varieties is a solution of particular interest to the farmer, as it does not require of him any additional work or investment in a product or equipment for treating the crop. Agricultural research is engaged in selecting new, increasingly resistant varieties.

Agricultural control

Agricultural control consists of encouraging rapid and proper development of the plant so as to make it more resistant to attack by pests (date of sowing, balanced fertilising, stubble ploughing, etc.). Agricultural control also fits in fairly well with the farmer's activities but is not always very effective.

Chemical control

Insecticides should not be used unless one is certain that it is worthwhile using them, as they are expensive products, which are cost-effective only if sufficient quantities of the insects are present.

Pressure from pests is generally moderate on upland rice of modest productivity. Chemical intervention is therefore seldom worthwhile and must be reserved solely for cases of highly productive, heavily infested crops.

Carbofuran (FURADAN) is currently the product most widely used, in the form of granules applied along the row of seeds at the time of sowing or during tillering at a rate of 800 g of active ingrediant per hectare.

Carrying out this operation is a delicate matter, as the product is potentially dangerous to the user. It is therefore advised that the recommendations on the packaging be followed scrupulously.

Biological control

Much research is currently being done into biological control, which uses useful insects or insect diseases to destroy harmful insects and this is a solution for the future.

Birds

Many species of small sparrows can prove to be very destructive by consuming the grains during the ripening phase. Bird-scaring guns are not very effective as the birds soon get used to the detonations. Although a demanding job, the only relatively satisfactory method is still to guard the crop (throwing stones, shouting, etc.). However, studies are underway to a view to using products to repel or lure the pests, which, combined with poisons will make it possible to destroy the birds that have been attracted, to smaller areas. The destruction of their roosts is also an effective but laborious procedure.

Rodents

Rodents (rats, mice, etc.) sometimes cause considerable damage to crops. One solution is to find out where the rodents nest and destroy them.

14 Harvesting

When to harvest

When rice is harvested depends partly on how it is to be used, i.e., whether it is for consumption or for seed.

In the former case, which is of course the more usual one, **account must be taken of the 'technological maturity', which corresponds to the highest yield from milling** (maximum percentage of whole milled grains). It depends on the variety used, the season and the cultivation

Fig 47   *Manual harvesting with a knife*

methods; that is why it is difficult to be categoric about the date of harvesting. However, 'technological maturity' may be assessed according to the appearance of the panicle. Technological maturity is attained if the yellow colouration covers two-thirds of the length of the axis (or rachis) of the panicle.

A more precise method consists of measuring the humidity of the grains. Maturity is attained when the grains have a water content of around 22%. In certain regions where the dry season is particularly marked at the time of maturity, the water content of the grains may be well below that figure at the time of harvesting which has a detrimental effect in terms of how the rice will stand up to milling.

It is important to harvest at the right time. If the rice is gathered too early, there is a loss in weight and many immature grains or 'green grains' are collected, which detracts from the value of the crop. If, however, the rice is gathered when it is over-ripe, there is considerable risk of shattering and breaking. Where the grains are to be used for seed, it is necessary to wait for 'physiological maturity', which corresponds to the maximum germinative capacity and energy. This occurs roughly seven to ten days after technological maturity. The water content is then around 19%.

Fig 48   *Bundles of panicles drying in the sun*

Harvesting methods

Manual harvesting:

- with a *knife*: here the farmer lifts only the panicles, which he puts together in bundles. This is a very slow operation, which may take as long as 100 h per hectare – on average you can count on 15 to 20 kg of rice per person per hour – which is why it is in the interests of the smallholder to stagger the dates when the varieties are sown or to grow varieties with different cycles, in order to avoid shattering. In order to make harvesting less laborious, it is preferable to use fairly tall glabrous (hairless) varieties;
- with a *sickle*: the sickle, which is not very widely used, does, however, make it possible to save time. Harvesting takes no more than 75 h/ha or thereabouts (25 to 35 kg of rice per person per hour). It would therefore be worth promoting the use of this implement, coupled with that of the cart, as the volume to be transported is then greater.

Mechanical harvesting:

- with a *cutterbar*, mounted on a two-wheeled tractor or a motor scythe, which harvest in swathes. With tractive power of 3 hp, it will take 13 hours to harvest a hectare. With 5 to 6 hp; this figure is reduced to 6 to 7 hours/ha.
- with a *reaper-binder*: this cuts the rice and makes it into sheaves, which then have to be dried and threshed;
- with a *combine harvester*, which cuts the straw and gathers and threshes the grain; this takes one or two hours per hectare;
- with a *'stripper'*, which removes only the panicles and leaves the straw standing. This equipment, which is still being studied has not come into widespread use at the present time.

Harvesters, whether they are reaper-binders or combines, and stripper represent a very substantial investment, which means that generally they can only be considered on a collective basis. The conditions under which such machines are used are also fairly restrictive. They require:
- easy access to the fields (width of tracks),
- a minimum plot size,
- correct soil conditions without variations in level or obstacles,
- careful maintenance,
- an elaborate infrastructure (supply of fuel, spare parts post-harvest treatment of the rice, etc.).

However, the timesaving with this type of equipment is considerable. The research institutes are endeavouring to develop equipment which will both harvest and thresh and which is suitable for medium – sized holdings (10 to 20 hectares), for which there are as yet no appropriate machines. It would appear that strippers are a possible future solution for this type of set-up; other equipment with an equivalent performance is also being constructed.

Drying

Drying is a particularly important operation if the rice is to be preserved without problems. It may be a crucial matter in certain countries with a high rainfall or in the case of short-cycle varieties harvested before the end of the rainy season.

At the time of harvesting, the grain is still very wet (it contains approximately 20% water). This figure must be reduced to 13%.

Drying techniques vary according to the way in which the rice has been harvested:
– bundles of panicles harvested manually: these may be dried suspended under a well-ventilated shelter;
– sheaves from the crop harvested using a sickle, motor scythe or reaper-binder: it is better not to leave the sheaves on the ground if it is wet as there is a risk of the grains germinating (most varieties of rice have grains which

Fig 49   *Drying rice in the sun*

are capable of germination shortly after harvesting) nor to expose them to rain which might still be possible, as the alternation between dessication and humidity causes the grains to break. Therefore, three methods are commonly used:

- **the stook**: six to eight sheaves are placed against one another vertically, with the panicles pointing upwards and are covered by an inverted sheaf to afford them protection.
- **perches**: the sheaves are placed against or on top of parallel bars fixed on to stakes approximately 80 cm from the ground.
- **slatted roofs**: the bundles rest on a roof formed of slats spaced at intervals. The panicles hang down between the slats and are thus protected.
- **the grain harvested by the stripper or combine**: this is artificially dried in 'ambient' or 'hot' air driers, in bulk or in sacks.

Threshing

Once the rice has been harvested and dried, the panicles have to be threshed.

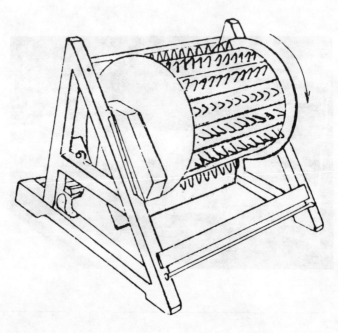

Fig 50 *Pedal-operated threshing drum (CEEMAT)*

The traditional technique consists of using sticks or flails. Sometimes, the sheaves are piled up in layers several sheaves thick and animals are used to tread out the rice.

In addition, there are a number of fixed threshers such as:
– the Japanese pedal-operated threshing drum, which has a throughput of some 70 kg of paddy per hour,
– the motorized thresher, which can handle 400 to 1500 kg of paddy, according to the output of the engine (7 to 30 hp). These threshers speed up the operation considerably compared with manual threshing, since a person can handle only 100 kg/day.

Generally, winnowing is still necessary in order to separate the heavy, well-filled grain from the straw waste, empty grains, etc. Here, wind is the traditional source of energy. In the case of mechanized harvesting, it is the combine or stripper which handles this operation and the threshing thus precedes the drying.

Fig 51 *Threshing the panicles*

How to preserve the rice

It is essential that the rice be preserved carefully away from water and insects

It is has been properly dried, the rice in the form of paddy (i.e., still

Fig 52   *Storage of rice in sacks*

enclosed by its glumellae) keeps better than milled rice. It is therefore better to store the grain in this state.

In theory, properly dried and aerated rice keeps well and does not require any special treatment

However, if there are preservation problems, a different procedure must be followed.

It is recommended that the grain store be disinfected with bromophos (280 ml of Nexion 36 CE® to 10 litres of water). The volume to be used per unit of area varies, according to the quality of the surface, from 100 to 300 ml/m².

Control of rice insects (plume-moths, weevils, etc.) then depends on the purpose for which the grain is to be used.

If the rice is to be used as seed, the sacks should be treated with pirim-phosmethyl (Actellic 50®) at a rate of 2 ml of commercial product per m² and followed with homogeneous powdering every three weeks with one kg of the product (Actellic 2%®) per tonne of grain. This treatment applies to wet regions; in dry regions, Nexion 2% should be used instead, at a rate of 500 g of commercial product per tonne.

If the rice is to be used for human consumption, it is preferable not to treat it at all. However, in the event of a significant invasion of harmful insects, treat with bromophos powder (Nexion 2P®) at a rate of 500 g of

Fig 53   *Damage by weevils to upland rice*

commercial product per tonne with a surface dressing every three weeks of
100 g of commercial product per m² of exterior surface area; fumigation is
carried out with hydrogen phosphide (Phostoxin®) at a dosage rate of one
tablet to 100 kg contained in an impervious container (plastic bucket,
drum).

Conclusion

In this handbook we have endeavoured to give technical prescription to
ease the passage from the traditional system practised by smallholders to a
more profitable system, either because this will lead them to cultivate
larger areas or because the anticipated yields are higher.

Accordingly, we have put the emphasis on varieties and on techniques
such as rotation, fertilising, mechanization, etc.

All these approaches must be thought about and adopted as part of an
integrated system. It is impossible to prescribe rigid combinations, as very
few would prove to be appropriate, given the diversity of the situations
encountered.

It will therefore be up to the farmer himself to devise his own

Time taken to perform various operations* with upland rice cultivation

	Manual cultivation	Draught animals	Appropriate tracted
LAND PREPARATION			
Ploughing		4 to 6 days/ha	1 day/ha
Preparation with tined implements		2 days/ha	3 h/ha
Reworking:			
cultivator		2 days/ha	3 h/ha
harrow		1 day/ha	1.5 h/ha
SOWING			
Dibbling	5 to 10 days/ha		
Broadcasting	2 to 5 days/ha		
Drilling	1 to 3 days/ha	0.5 day/ha	2 to 2.5 h/ha
WEEDING (pre pass)			
Pulling of weeds	40 to 60 days/ha		
Chemical weeding	1 day/ha		
Hoeing	daba: 15 to 20 days/ha	2 to 4 days/ha	3 to 4 h/ha
FERTILISER SPREADING	1 day/ha		0.5 h/ha
HARVESTING	Knife: 15 to 20 kg/h		Motor scythe: 6 to 15 h/ha
	Sickle: 25 to 35 kg/h		Reaper-binder: 2 to 3 h/ha
THRESHING	Flail, stick: 100 kg/day		Motorized thresher 400 to 1 500 kg/ (according to output of engine)
	Pedal-operated thresing drum: 70 kg/h		
SIMULTANEOUS THRESHING AND HARVESTING			Combines, Stripper 1 to 2 h/ha

* These figures are norms obtained by taking an average of the time needed to perform various operations, measured the different locations and under different conditions. The actual time taken may vary according to the specific situation (type of equipment, condition of the soil, farmer's technical skill, etc.).

combination of cultural technical practises in accordance with his technical ability and financial resources, combining as he sees fit, the means that have been placed at his disposal and whose advantages and drawbacks we have explained. It is the extension worker who will have the task of advising the farmer and helping him in his choices.

Economic circumstances will sometimes make it necessary to push certain agricultural principles into the background. This point must also be taken into consideration by the fieldworker, who will be aware of the real situation (prices, markets, etc.) in the area in which he works.

Fig 54   *Intensively cultivated upland rice*

Glossary

Blast disease in rice caused by a fungus.

Booting stage of development during which the panicles rise up the sheath. Booting follows panicle initiation and precedes heading.

Buffer strips strips 1 m to 3 m wide which follow the contour lines and have vegetation growing on them in order to reduce or slow down run-off

Certified seed seed obtained under the supervision of an official body which meets certain quality requirements.

Compost mixture of organic waste and earth converted by fermentation which may serve as fertiliser.

Contour line line joining points of equal altitude; contour lines are used to depict relief on maps.

Conventional tractors all high output tractors (more than 15 hp) with attachments.

Critical period period when rice is particularly sensitive to a lack of water. Flowering is a critical period for rice.

Crop residues straw remaining in the field after harvesting.

Deficiency absence or inadequacy in the plant's nutrition of certain elements required for its development.

Density number of plants per unit of area.

Fallow land temporarily left to rest, without being cultivated.

Fumigation action of producing disinfecting fumes or vapour.

Fungicide chemical used to destroy the diseases which attack plants.

Glumellae covering of the rice flower, removed with the husk during milling.

Groundwater underground water-bearing bed created by the percolation of rainwater or river water; it can supply the rice with water if its level is close to the surface of the ground.

Harrow implement for working the soil (mainly for secondary cultivations) which operates at a shallow depth using rigid vertical pointed tines without shares.

Heading: stage in the development of rice when the panicle emerges from the leaf sheath.

Herbicide chemical used to destroy weeds.

Hoeing operation consisting of removing weeds; it is accompanied by loosening of the top soil with the implement used.

Leaching impoverishment of the soil caused by the action of water, which dissolves certain nutrients and carries them deep down, making them useless for the plant.

Lignify take on the consistency of wood.

Lodging effect of the wind, disease or excessive fertility which flattens plants in the field.

Marigot low-lying area subject to flooding in the rainy season

Mineral toxicity excessive presence of a mineral, which acts as a poison to the plant.

Multicultivator versatile equipment consisting of two parts: i. a single body, to which various implements are attached; ii. various attachments, which are specific implements for one or more operations, such as ploughs, cultivator tines, harrows, drills, seeders, fertiliser distributors and even cart platforms (only polycultivator), etc. There are a number of models which can be used with draught animals and small tractors: multicultivators without stabilization (e.g., Knoll); multicultivators with longitudinal stabilization (Sine, Arara, etc.), which are the most widespread as they are the simplest and cheapest; the Ariana multicultivator, with longitudinal and transverse stabilization; olycultivators ('tropicultivator', high-output poly-cultivator, etc), which, because they are expensive, are far less widespread.

Nozzle part of a sprayer fitted with an aperture of a given shape, which makes it possible to dose and apply accurately the product being distributed.

Organic matter plant nutrient originating from a living body, whether animal or vegetable.

Panicle all the spikelets on a stem.

Panicle initiation stage in the development of rice during which the formation of panicles commences. Panicle initiation is followed by booting.

pH figure denoting soil acidity. An acid soil has a pH lower than 7; a chalky soil has a pH of more than 7.

Physiological maturity stage when the rice grain is most likely to yield a high-energy seed with good germinative capacity; this is when the rice should be harvested if it is to be used for seed.

Phytotoxicity effect of poisoning a cultivated plant by the action of herbicides.

Polycultivator particular model of multicultivator which has large wheels, enabling it to be used as a cart if a load platform is attached.

Pressure from pests extent of insect attack.

Ripening stage in the development of rice during which the grains fill out. Ripening culminates in harvesting.

Rolling cultural operation consisting of going over the ground with a roller in order to compact the topsoil.

Rotary crushing grinding up plants or straw with a rotating implement fitted with blades which is attached to the tractor's power take-off.

Rotation succession of different crops on the same plot in a fixed sequence.

Share triangular piece of metal which cuts through the soil horizontally and digs a furrow.

Small tractors all machinery with a low output (less than 15 hp) with the corresponding attachments.

Soil-erosion barrier device to control erosion consisting of buffer strips where successive ploughing with the earth always being turned over downhill leads to a gradual levellin out of the surface.

Soil horizon a layer of soil of varying depth and uniform consistency. All the horizons superimposed one on top of another constitute the soil profile.

Soil profile   see 'soil horizon'.

Spacing   distance separating two plants or two rows of plants.

Spikelet   flower; each spikelet yields a grain.

Spreading   action of distributing manure on a soil in order to fertilise it.

Stubble ploughing   burying the stubble (i.e., the straw remaining on the field after harvesting) with a plough.

Technological maturity   stage when the rice grain is likely to give a good yield upon milling (maximum percentage of whole milled grains); this is when the rice should be harvested if it is to be milled.

Tiller   secondary shoot forming at the base of a plant's main stem. The secondary shoots in turn send forth tillers.

Tillering   stage in the growth of cereals when they send forth secondary shoots.

Top cultivations   working the soil to a depth not exceeding 10 cm.

Topicultivator   see 'Multicultivator'.

Working down   surface cultivation following another type of cultivation and intended to prepare the final seedbed.

Index

multicultivators, 46
    for weeding, 67

nitrogen, 48
    and staggered ripening, 24
Nstar CE 250, 73
nutrients, 48

one-way ploughing, 39

paddy, preservation of, 85
panicle initiation, 21
perch drying, 84
pests, 14
phosphorus, 48
    deficiency, 55
physiological maturity, 81
pioneer system of cultivation, 8–9
ploughing, 37–39
    with animals, 42–3
    depth, 40
    direction, 41
    and erosion, 39, 41
    mechanized, 43
    time for, 88
    timing of, 40–1
    types, 39
    width, 40
post-emergence herbicides, 73
potassium, 48
pre-emergence herbicides, 72
preservation of rice, 85–6
production, and price, 15

rainfall, 16
    and herbicide application, 72
    and rotation, 35
reaper-binder, 82
reduced tillage
    with discs, 45–6
    with tined equipment, 44–5
Reforan CE 30, 73
rice
    predecessors of, 34
    price of, and production, 15
    varieties of, 20–1
        and insect resistance, 78
rodents, as pests, 79

rotation, 33–4
    examples of, 35
    and weeds, 66
round and round ploughing, 39
round-up, 74
rows, spacing of, and weeding, 67,
    68

secondary tillage, 46–7
seed drill, adjustment of, 62–3
seed harvesting, and maturity, 80–1
seedbed, characteristics of, 46
seeds
    certified, 57
    selected, 65
semi-mechanized cultivation, 10
Senegal, routine fertilising in, 53
shifting cultivation, 6
sickle, 82
slatted roof drying, 84
soil
    acidity, 12, 54–5
    firming of, 58
    mineral deficiencies in, 55
        and fertiliser, 52
    preparation, 36–7
        time for, 88
        and weeds, 65–6
    suitable, 16–17
soil coverage, 27
sorghum, as predecessor, 34
sowing, 58–64
    depth of, 58
    time for, 88
    timing of, 26, 57–8
sowing density, 61, 63
    and gully erosion, 17
    and weeds, 66
spacing, of rows, 61–2
spinning-disc sprayers, 71
sprayers, 69–71
    adjustment of, 72
spring-tined cultivators, 45
staggered ripening, 24
Stam F 34, 73
stem borers, 76–7
stook drying, 84
straight fertilisers, 49

strictly upland rice cultivation, 3–4,
  5
stripper, 82
swing ploughs, 44–5

texture, of soil, 16
thioral, 57
threshing, 84–5
  time for, 88
tillage
  mechanical, 10
  secondary, 46–7
tillering, 21
  and fertiliser application, 50
  water requirement during, 25
tillers, 45
tined implements, time-scale for
  using, 88
total herbicides, 74–5
tractors
  and crop spraying, 71
  and reduced tillage, 45
  and secondary tillage, 47
  see also mechanization
Turn CE 50, 73

upland rice cultivation, 3–5
upland rice varieties, 21

varieties, selection of, 27–9

water, 16; *see also* rainfall
water requirement
  and growth cycle, 25–6
  and sowing, 57–8
weeding, 7
  with animals, 67
  chemical
    between crops, 74–5
    during cultivation, 68–73
  manual, 66–7
  mechanized, 68
  and seed spacing, 61–2
  time for, 88
weeds, 11
  and cultivation techniques,
    65–6
  and fertiliser application, 52
  and ploughing, 38
  pre-cultivation precautions
    against, 66
  and reduced tillage, 44
  and secondary tillage, 46
width, for ploughing, 40
wind, and herbicide application,
  72
winnowing, 85

yield
  and row spacing, 61
  and timing of sowing, 58